READING

Triumphs

INTERVENTION

Practice Book

Annotated Teacher's Edition

Program Authors

Dr. Jan E. Hasbrouck
Educational Consultant
J. H. Consulting
Seattle, Washington

Dr. Janice A. Dole
University of Utah
Salt Lake City, Utah

Macmillan
McGraw-Hill

A

The McGraw·Hill Companies

Published by Macmillan/McGraw-Hill, of McGraw-Hill Education, a division of The McGraw-Hill Companies, Inc., Two Penn Plaza, New York, New York 10121.

Printed in the United States of America

2 3 4 5 6 7 8 9 10 007 10 09 08 07 06

Contents

Unit 1

Unit 2

Unit 6

Unit 7

Unit 8

Unit 9

Unit 10

Name ______________________________

		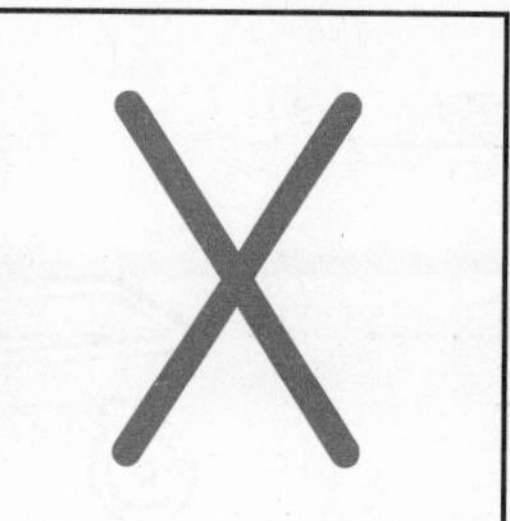	

			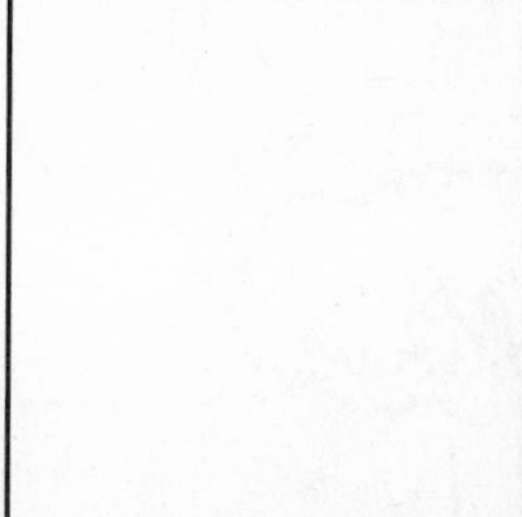

		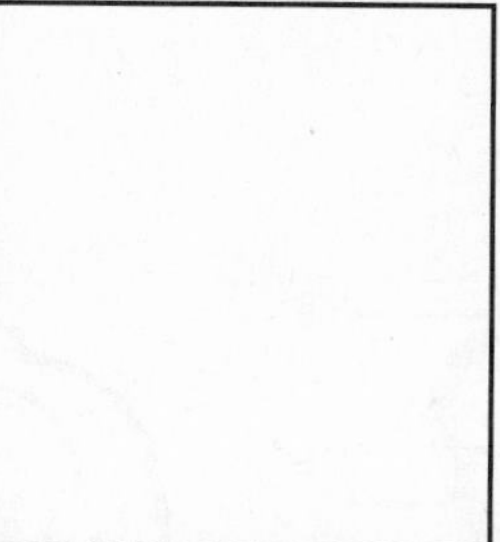	

Phonological Awareness

 Mark an X in each box to show how many words are in the sentence I say: *I play ball.*

 *Horses run fast.*  *Mom sings.*  *I write my name.*

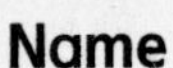

Name ______________________________

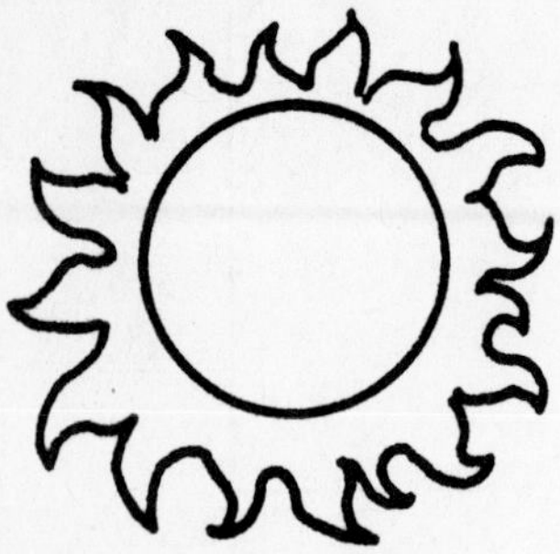

1 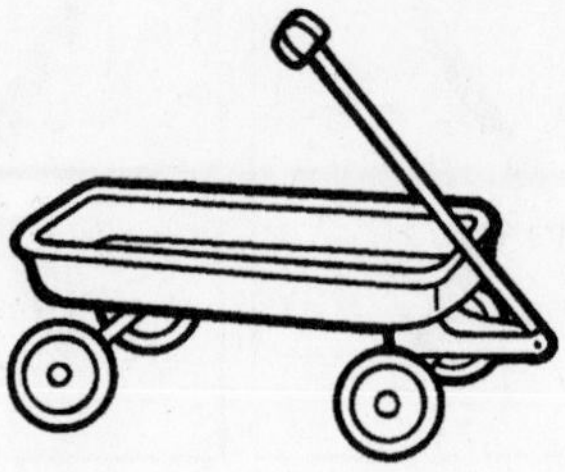 2

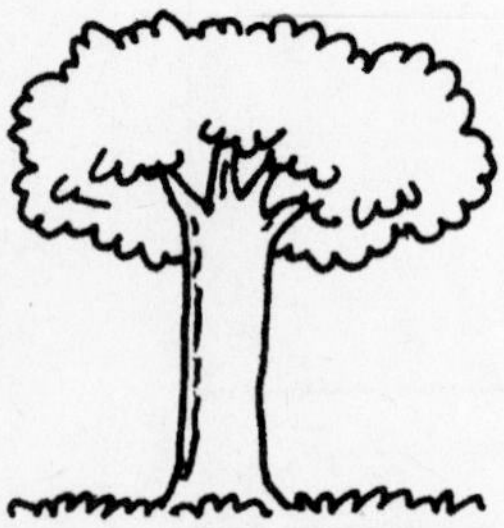

1 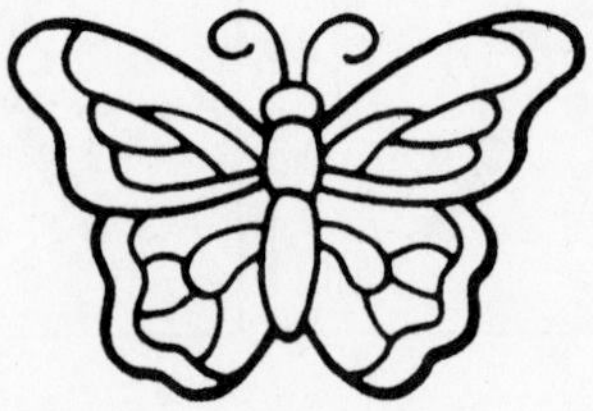 3

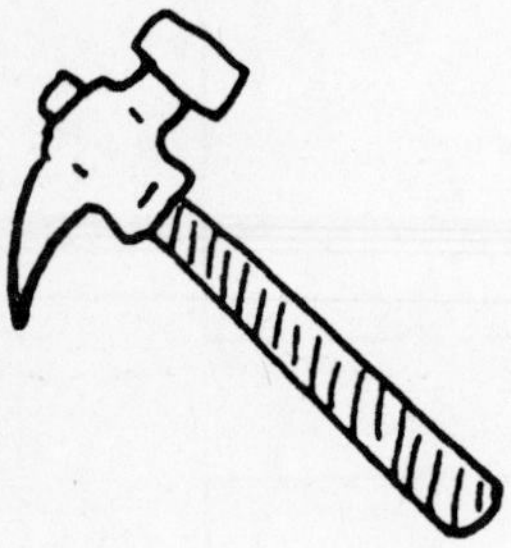

2 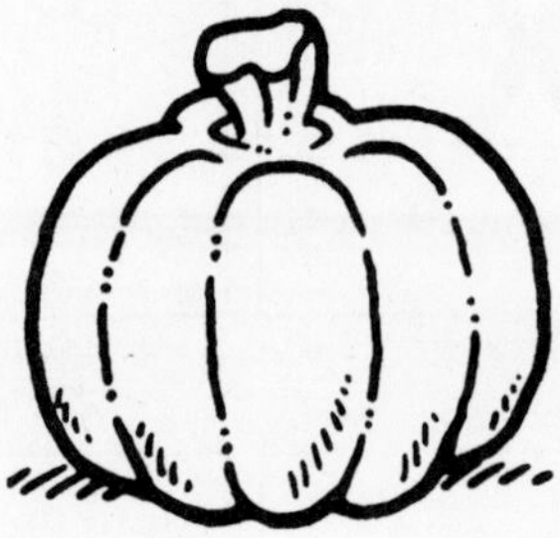 2

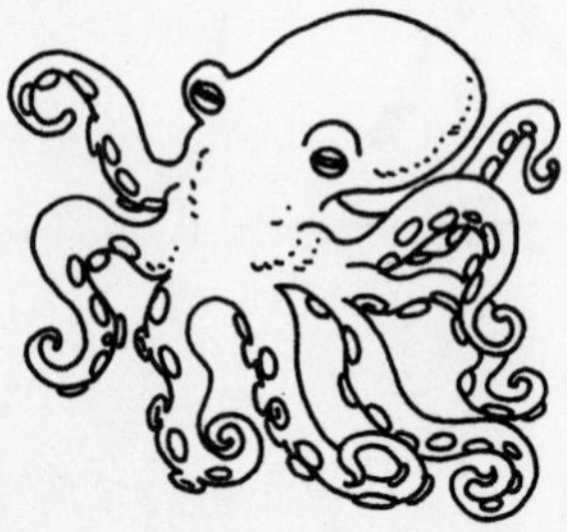

3 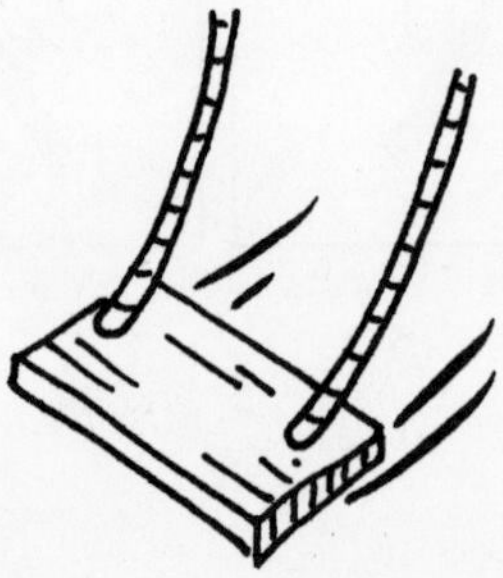 1

Phonemic Awareness

Say each picture's name and clap the number of syllables you hear.
Then write the number of syllables on the line.

Name ______________________________

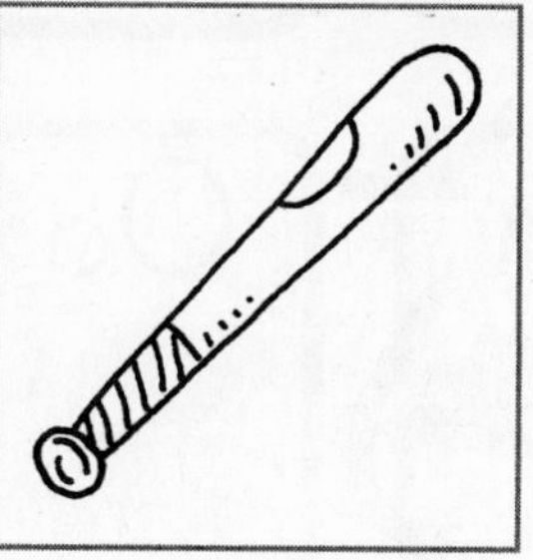

Phonemic Awareness

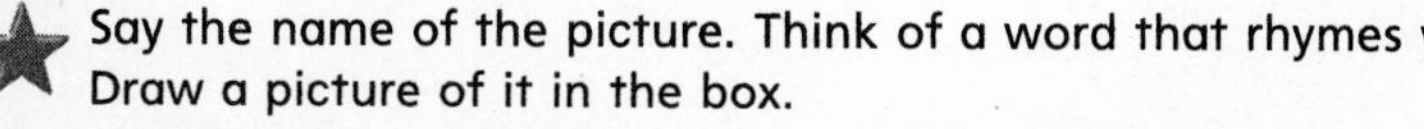

Say the name of the picture. Draw a line to the picture with a name that rhymes.

Say the name of the picture. Think of a word that rhymes with *pen*.
Draw a picture of it in the box.

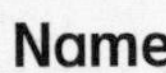

Name ______________________________

The Alphabet

Aa

Bb

Cc

Dd

Ee

Ff

Gg

Hh

Ii

Jj

Kk

Ll

Mm

Nn

Oo

Pp

Qq

Rr
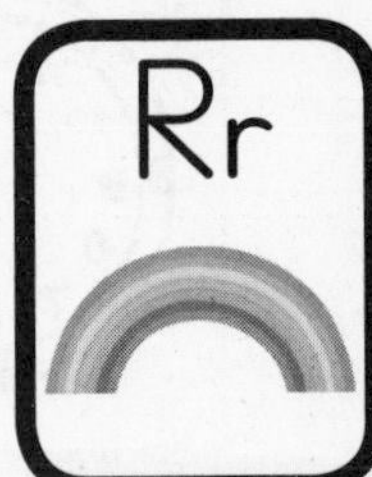

Ss

Tt

Uu

Vv

Ww

Xx

Yy

Zz

Alphabet Recognition

Sing the Alphabet Song. Then color in the first letter of your name.

Name ________________________________

To the Teacher:
Have children tell what happens to the Gingerbread Boy.

The Gingerbread Boy

To the Teacher:
Have children tell how the old woman and man are feeling. Ask why they feel that way.

To the Teacher:

Have children predict whether the woman and man will catch the Gingerbread Boy.

To the Teacher:

Have children color the fox orange.

Write

Name

Writing

Build your name with Letter Cards.

Write your name.

Write your name again. Trace over each letter in a different color crayon.

Name ______________________________

Oral Language

Name the pictures in each box. Then cut out the pictures on the side of the page. Glue each picture in the box where it belongs.

Name ___________________________________

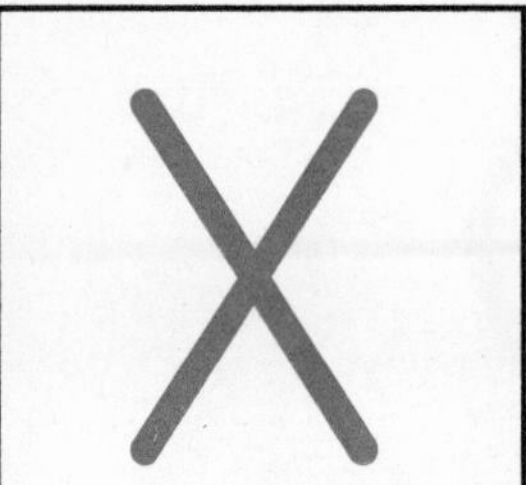

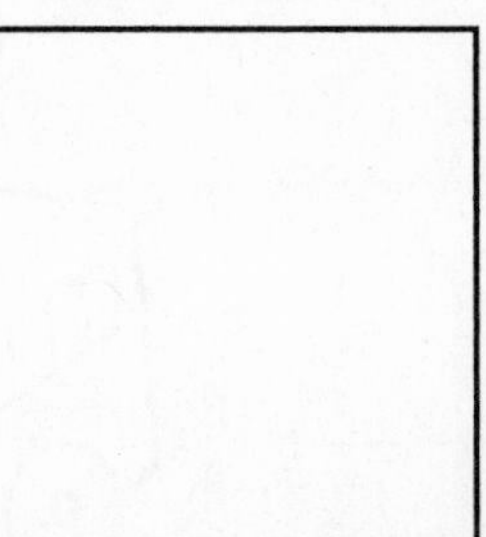

Phonological Awareness

 Mark an X in each box to show how many words are in the sentence I say: *I go to school.*

 *Sam skates.*  *My bike is red.* *I eat apples.*

Name ______________________________

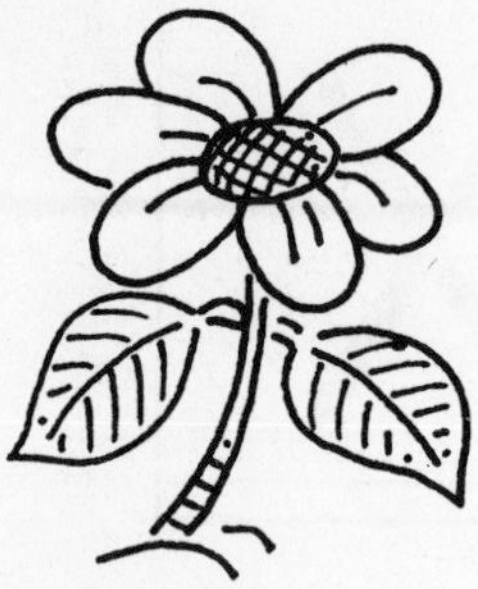

2 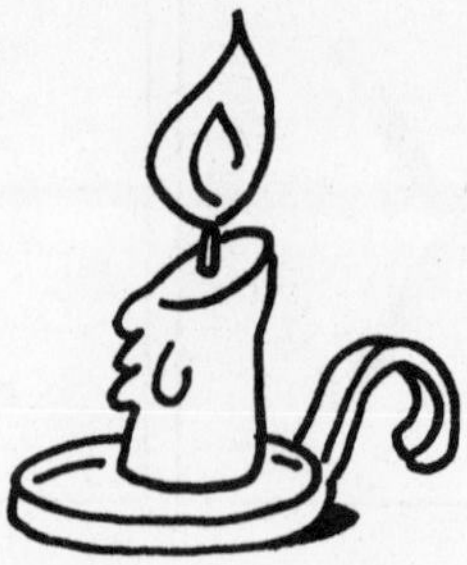 2

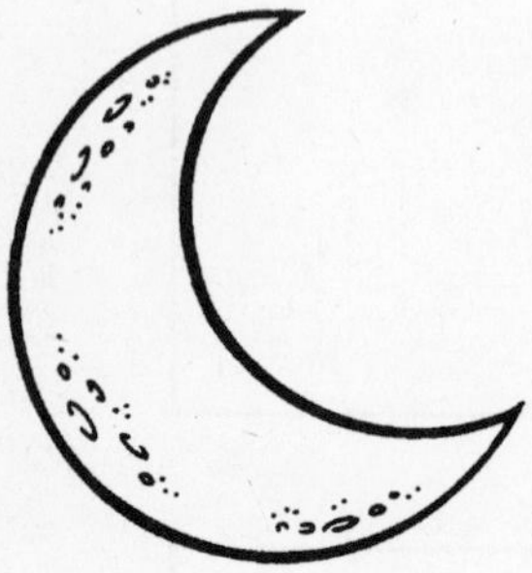

1 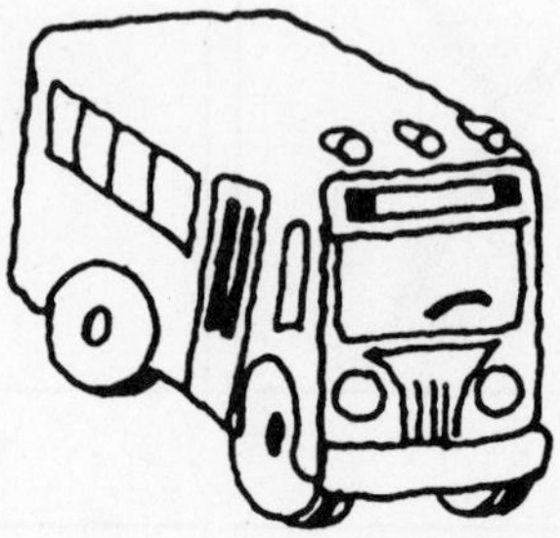 1

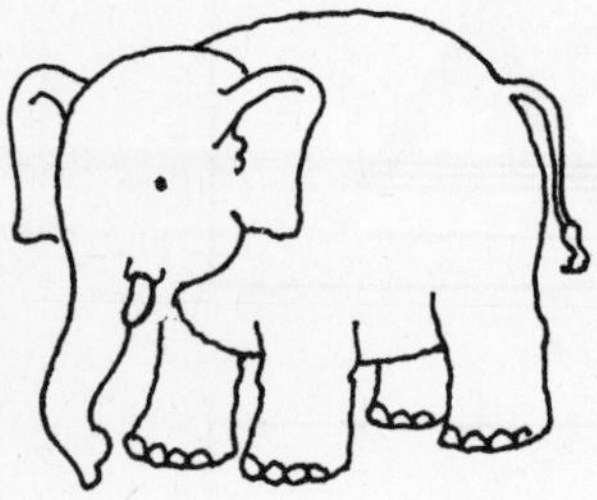

3 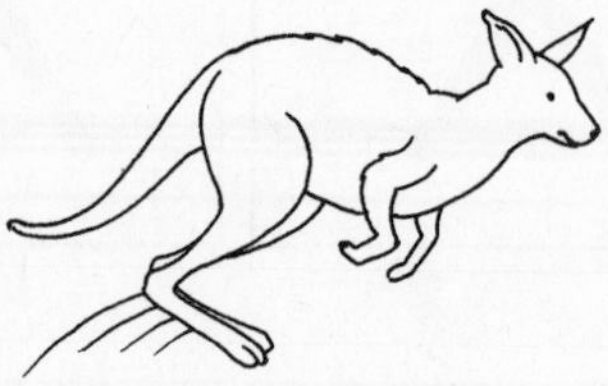 3

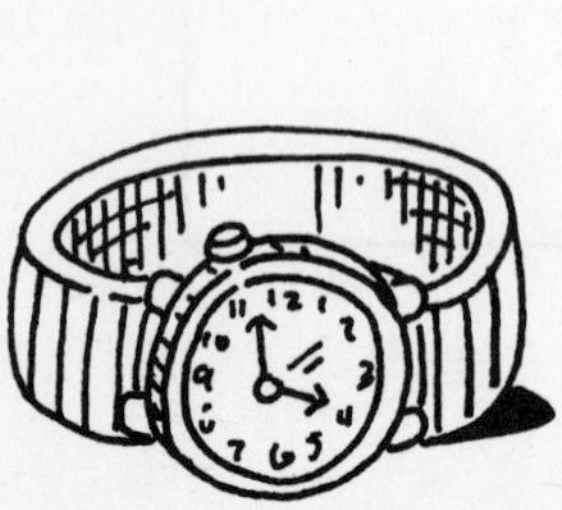

1 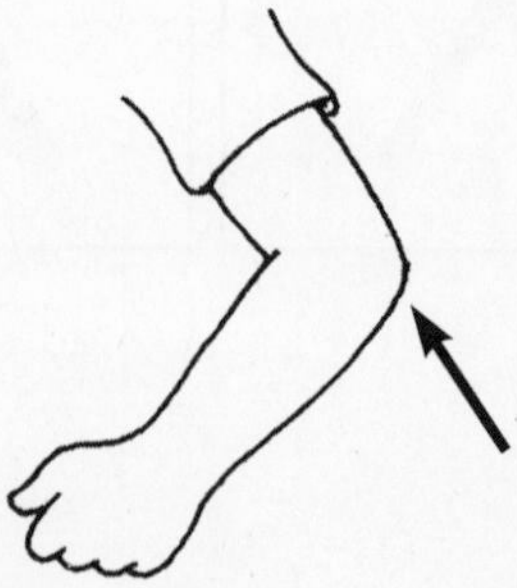 2

Phonemic Awareness

Say each picture's name and clap the number of syllables you hear. Then write the number of syllables on the line.

Name ____________________

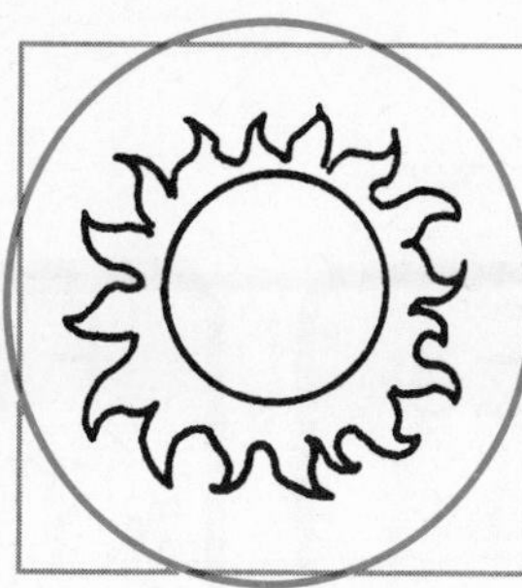

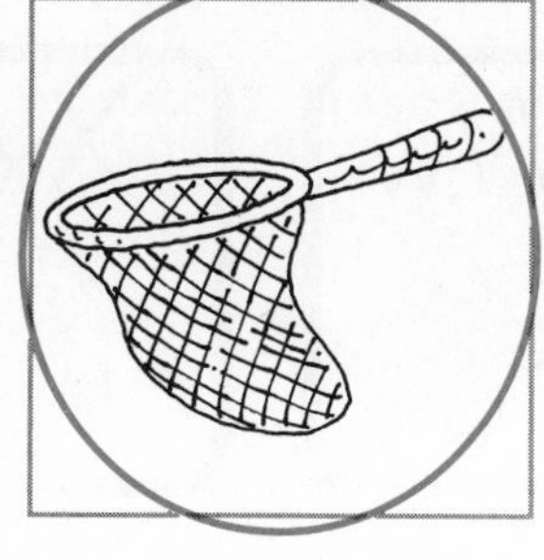
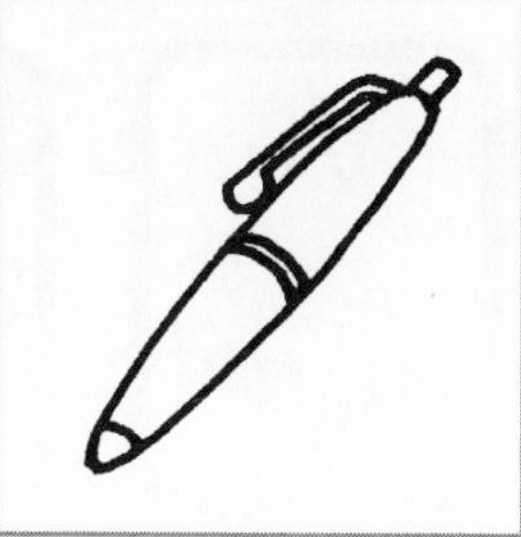

Phonemic Awareness

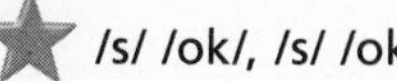 Listen as I say a word in parts. Then find and circle the picture: /s/ /un/, /s/ /un/.

 /s/ /ok/, /s/ /ok/  /k/ /at/, /k/ /at/  /n/ /et/, /n/ /et/ 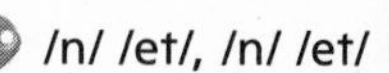  /b/ /ed/, /b/ /ed/

Name ____________________

The Alphabet

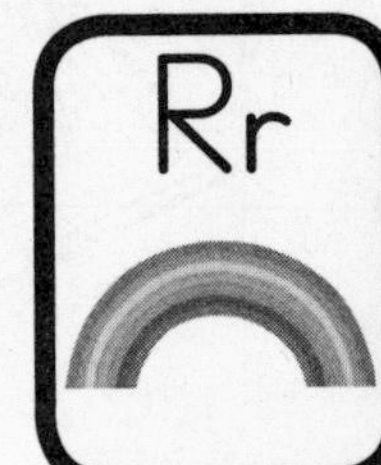

Alphabet Recognition

Sing the Alphabet Song together as children point to each letter on the page. Write one letter pair on the board for each child to name. Then have them find and color those letters on the page.

Name ______________________________

To the Teacher:

Have children draw the giant carrot and color it orange.

The Carrot

To the Teacher:

Have children tell where the man is. Then have them color the leafy carrot top green.

To the Teacher:

Have children tell what the man is trying to do. Ask children to tell why they think he is doing this.

To the Teacher:

Have children predict what will happen next.

Write

Name ____________________

Writing

Build your name using all uppercase Letter Cards. Write your name.

Use a different uppercase letter to change the first letter in your name to make a silly name.

Name ______________________________

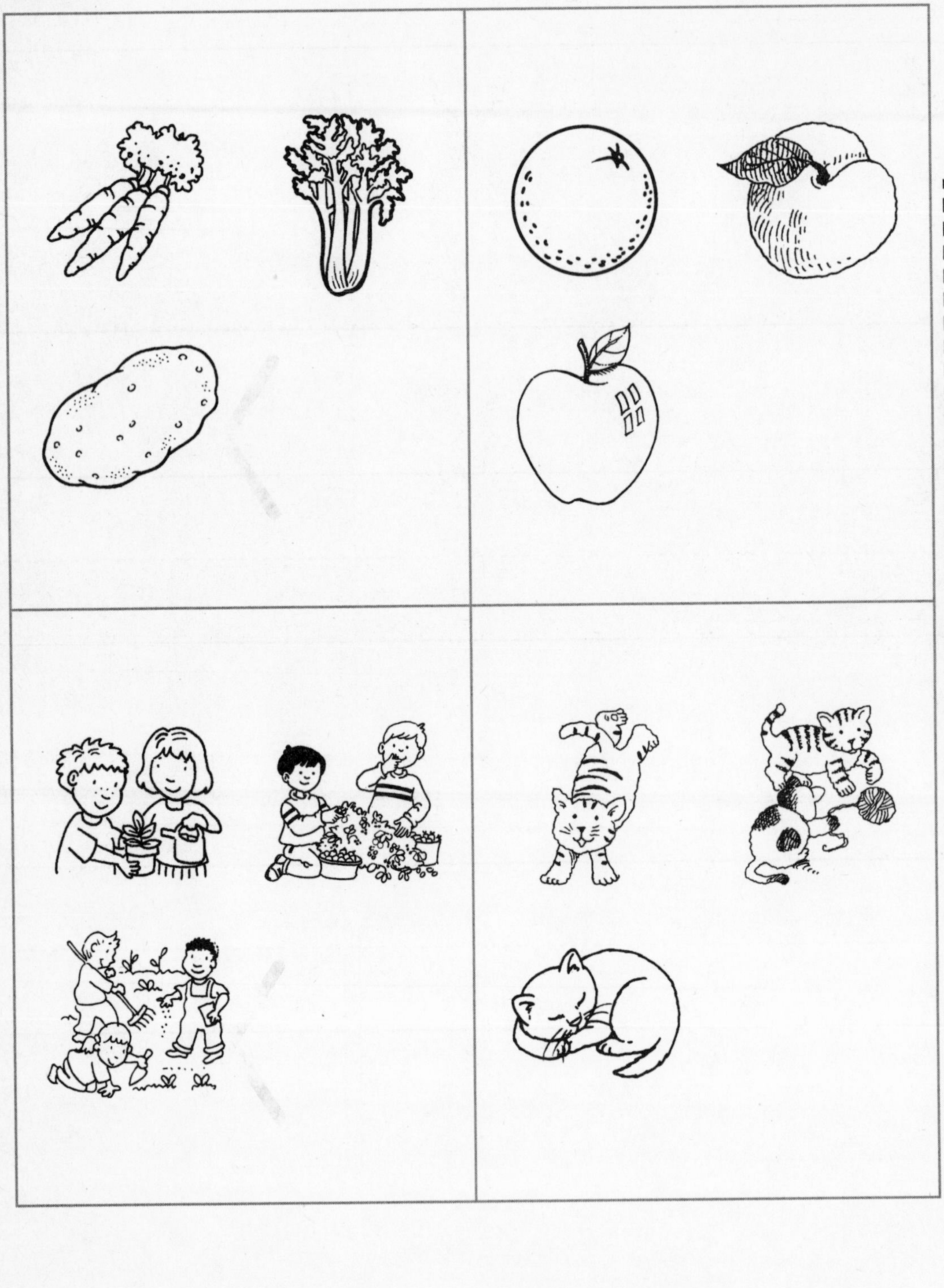

Oral Language

Name the pictures in each box. Then cut out the pictures on the side of the page. Glue each picture in the box where it belongs.

Name ______________________________

Phonological Awareness

 Mark an X in each box to show how many words are in the sentence I say: *I draw pictures.*

 *Meg has a dog.*  *Cats climb trees.* *Ants have six legs.*

Name ______________________________

Phonemic Awareness

 Say the name of the picture. Draw a line to the picture with a name that rhymes.

 Say the name of the picture. Think of a word that rhymes with *hat*. Draw a picture of it in the box.

Name ____

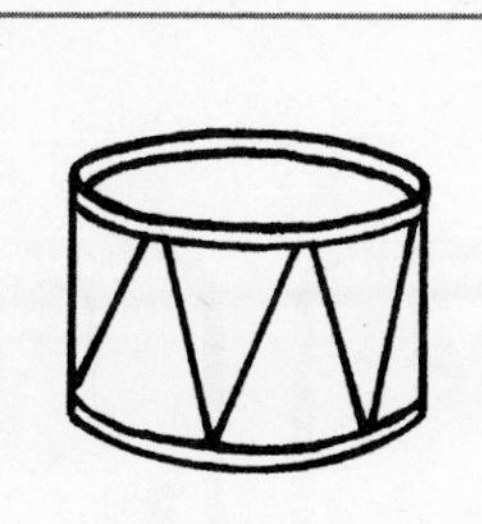  

 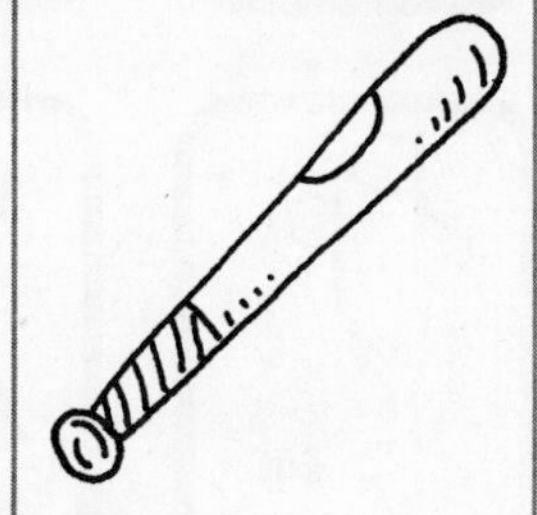 

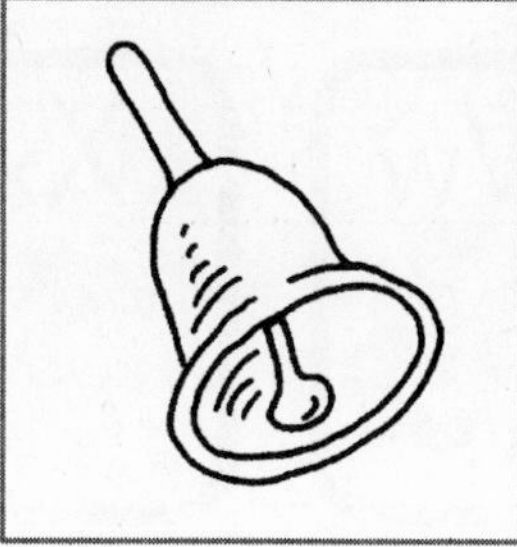 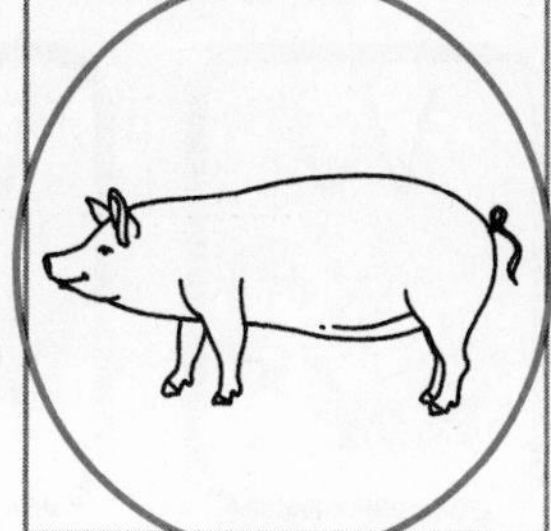 

Phonemic Awareness

 Listen as I say a word in parts. Then find and circle the picture: /d/ /uk/, /d/ /uk/.

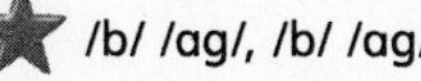 /b/ /ag/, /b/ /ag/  /k/ /up/, /k/ /up/ 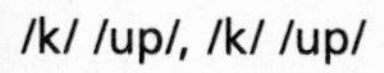  /p/ /ig/, /p/ /ig/ 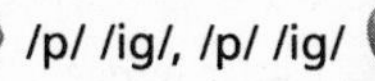  /n/ /est/, /n/ /est/

Name ______________________________

The Alphabet

Aa

Bb

Cc

Dd

Ee

Ff

Gg

Hh

Ii

Jj

Kk

Ll

Mm

Nn

Oo

Pp

Qq

Rr
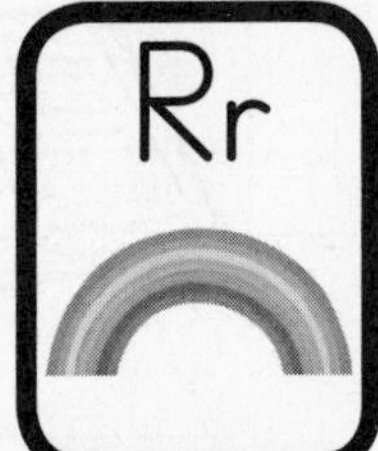

Ss

Tt

Uu

Vv

Ww

Xx

Yy

Zz

Alphabet Recognition

Point to each letter on the page as we sing the Alphabet Song. Then look around the classroom to find letters on labels or in print. As you find a letter, circle it on the page.

Name ______________________________

To the Teacher:
Have children draw a baby bird in the nest.

Birds

To the Teacher:
Have children tell what the bird is doing, and why.

To the Teacher:

Have children tell what the bird is doing now. Then have them put an X on the egg.

To the Teacher:

Have children predict what they think will happen next.

Write

Name ______________________________

Writing

 Build your name using uppercase and lowercase Letter Cards. Turn each Letter Card facedown. Ask a partner to turn over and name each letter in your name.

 Write your name as your partner watches.  Ask your partner to write your name.

Cut

Name ______________________________

Oral Language

Name the pictures in each box. Then cut out the pictures on the side of the page. Glue each picture in the box where it belongs.

Name ____________________

I  !

mop

___op

To the Teacher:

Have children reread the book, then write or trace the letters and words in the gray boxes.

I Mix

I  .

mix

M M M

I (mix) .

I (mix) .

Name ______________________________

m

m  m

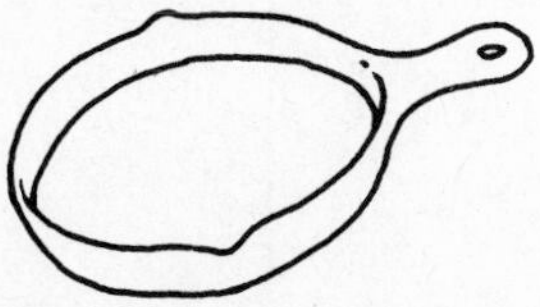

m

m

Phonics

Say the picture name. If the picture name begins with the /m/ sound, write *m* on the line.

Name

1. I  .

2. I  .

3.  .

High-Frequency Words

1–2: Read and trace the sentences.

3: Write the sentence I ____ . Draw a picture in the box of something you do.

Name ______________________

I ____ .

mop

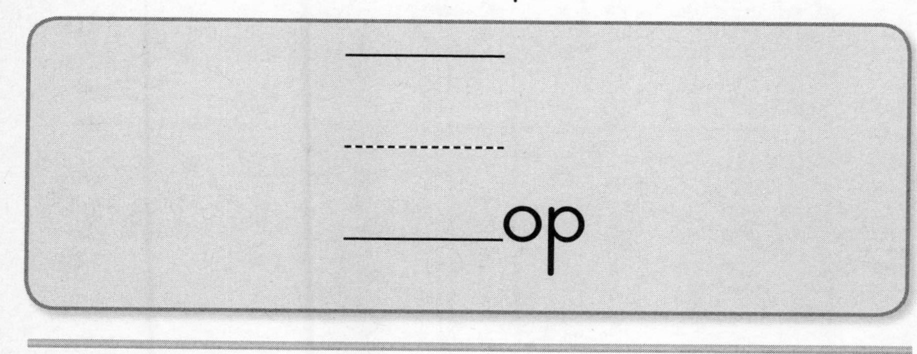

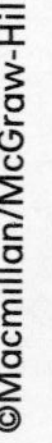

To the Teacher:

Have children reread the book, then write or trace the letters and words in the gray boxes.

I Mop

I  .

mix

I mop.

mop

m m m

I  mix.

mix

mix

Name ____________________

I can !
swim

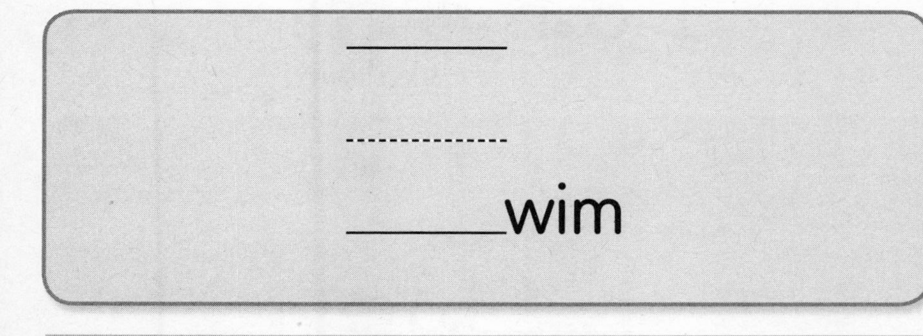

To the Teacher:
Have children reread the book, then write or trace the letters and words in the gray boxes.

I Can!

I can  !
slide

I can swing !

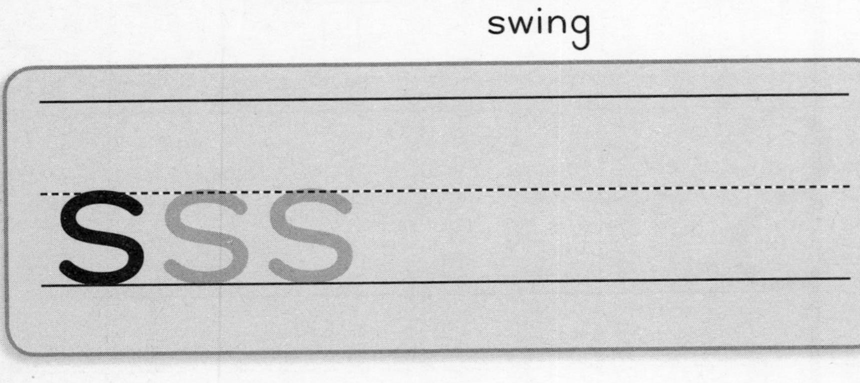

S s s

I can  skate !

skate

Name ______________________________

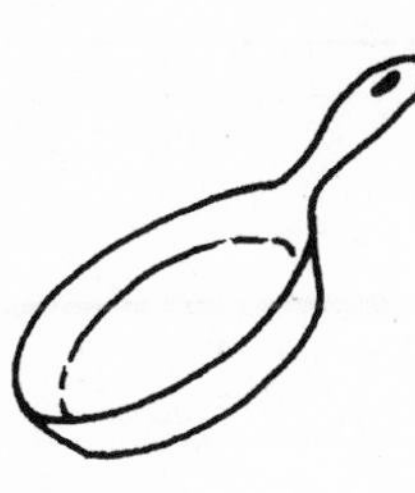

Phonics

Say the picture name. If the picture name begins with the /s/ sound, write *s* on the line.

Name

I can.

High-Frequency Words

Read the sentence. Write the sentence. Draw a picture of something that you can do.

Name ______________________________

I can  .

sleep

To the Teacher:
Have children reread the book, then write or trace the letters and words in the gray boxes.

I Can

I can  .

sing

S S S

I can swim.

S S S

I can swing.

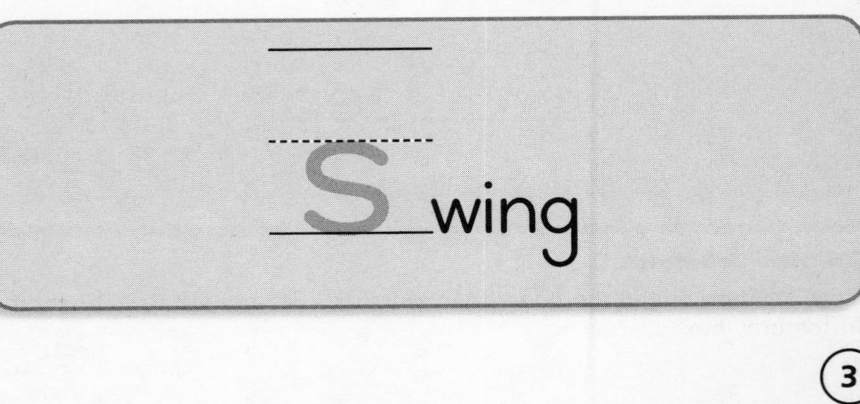

S wing

Name ______________________

Can I sit ?

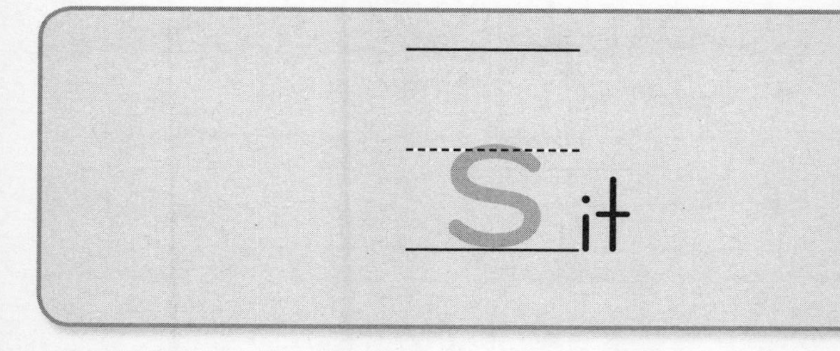

To the Teacher:
Have children reread the book, then write or trace the letters and words in the gray boxes.

Can I?

Can I mop?

Can I  mix?

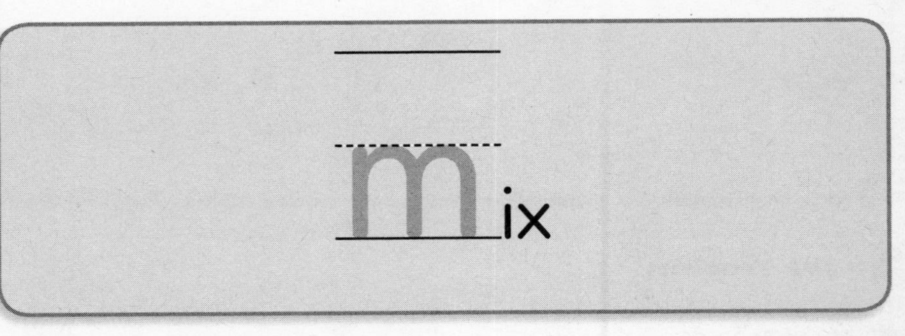

Name ______________________________

s

m

m

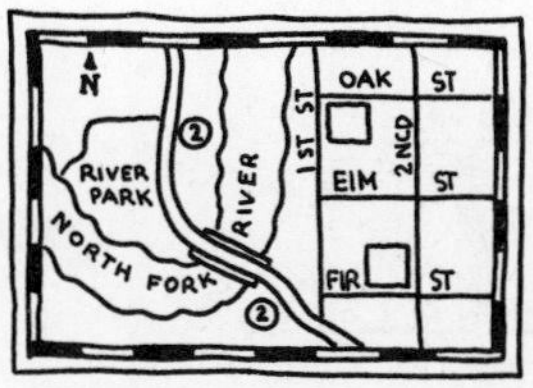

m

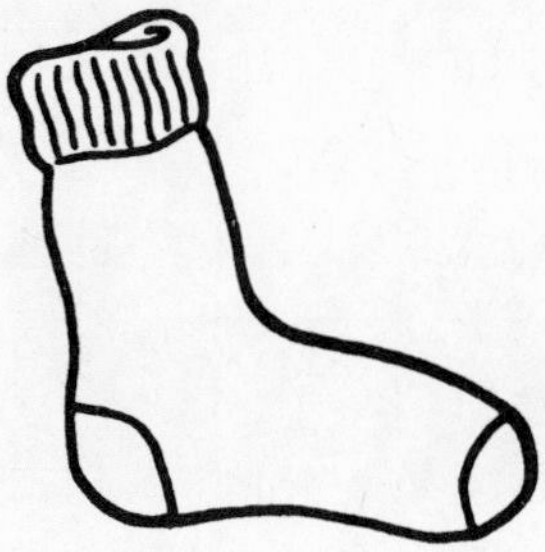

s

s

m

m

Phonics

Say the picture name. If the picture name begins with the /m/ sound, write *m* on the line. If the picture name begins with the /s/ sound, write *s* on the line.

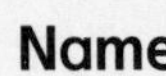

Name ______________________

1. I can  .

2. I can  .

3. I can  .

4. I can  .

High-Frequency Words

1: Read the sentence.

2–3: Trace the words and read the sentences.

4: Write *I can* and read the sentence.

Name ______________________

I can!

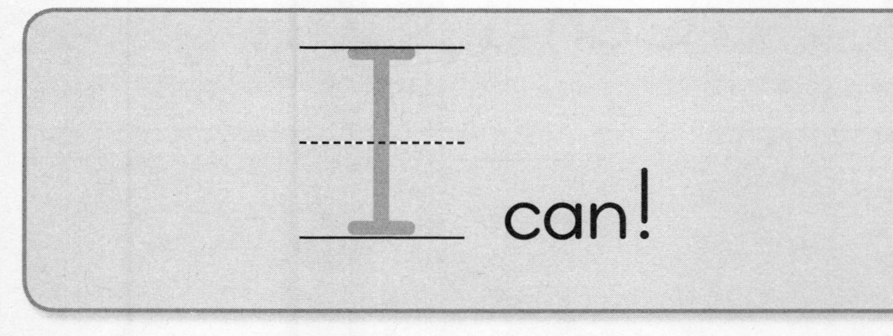

To the Teacher:
Have children reread the book, then write or trace the letters and words in the gray boxes.

I Can!

Can I  ?
sew

S S S

I can!

Can I  ?
mix

Name ______________________________

We can pop!

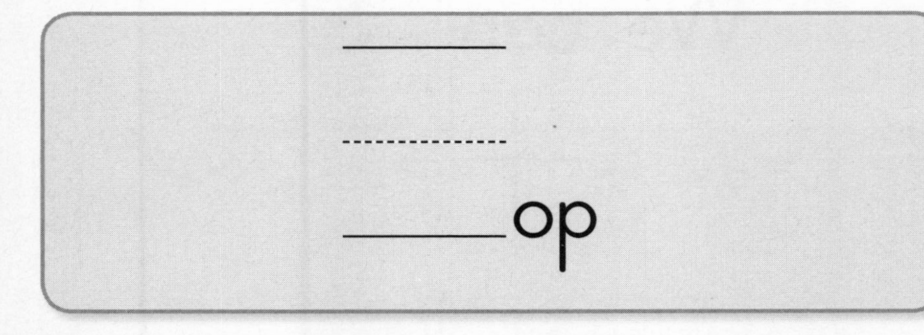

To the Teacher:
Have children reread the book, then write or trace the letters and words in the gray boxes.

We Can

We can  .
pin

We can [pin].

pin

p p p

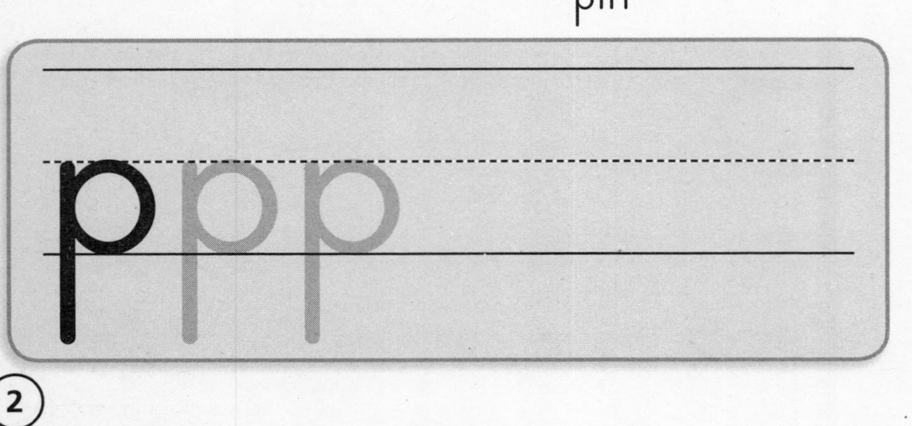

We can [pin].

pin

pin

Name

PPPP

pppp

Phonics

 Say the picture name. If the picture begins with the /p/ sound, write *p* on the line.

 Trace and then write both uppercase *P* and lowercase *p* three more times.

Name ______________________________

We  .

We  .

We  .

We  .

High-Frequency Words

 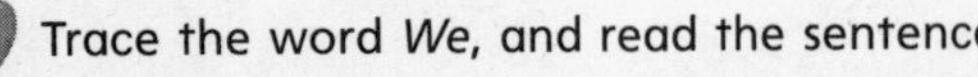
Trace the word *We*, and read the sentence.  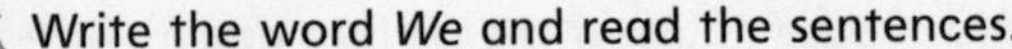
Write the word *We* and read the sentences.

Write the word *We*. Draw your own picture in the box to complete the sentence. Read the sentence.

Name ____________________

We can [pin] .

pin

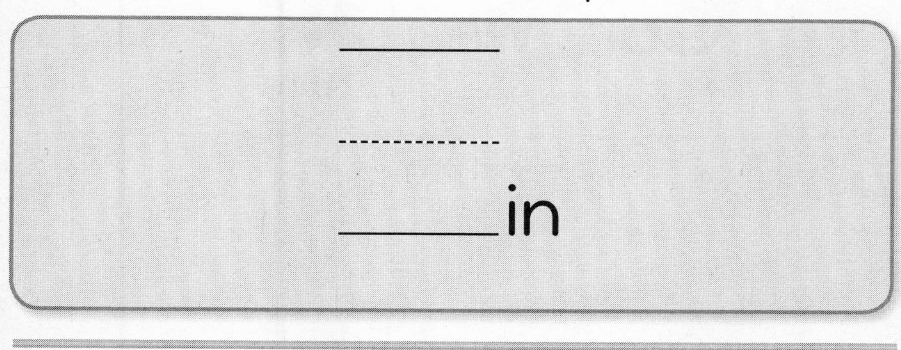

______

______in

To the Teacher:

Have children reread the book, then write or trace the letters and words in the gray boxes.

Can We?

Can we [paint] ?

paint

P P P P

We can  paint.

paint

p p p

Can we  pin?

pin

___in

Name ____________________

We like 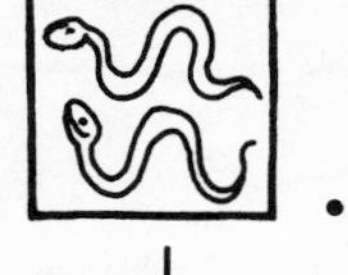 .

snakes

To the Teacher:

Have children reread the book, then write or trace the letters and words in the gray boxes.

We Like!

We like  .

tigers

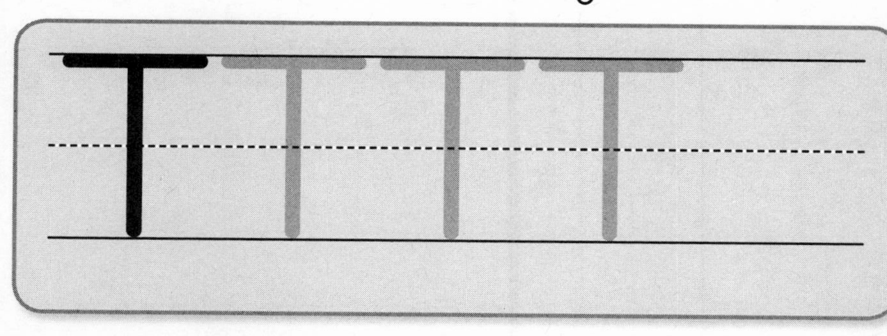

We like  turkeys.

ttt

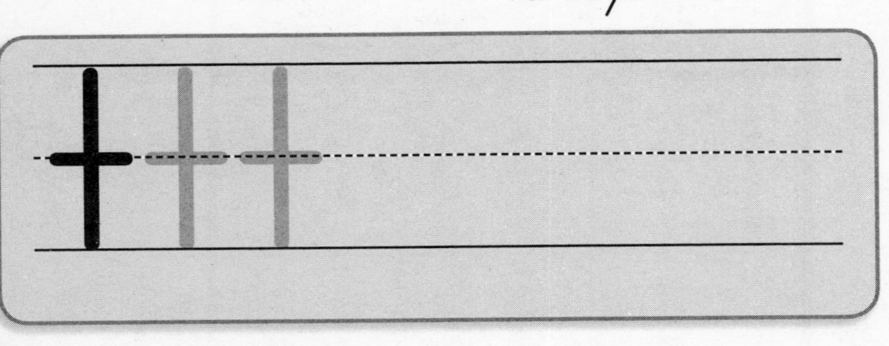

We like  turtles.

____urtles

Name ______________________________

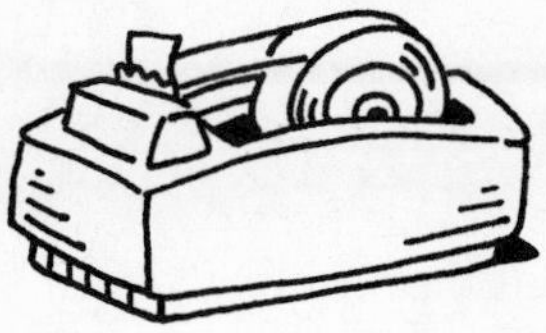

t

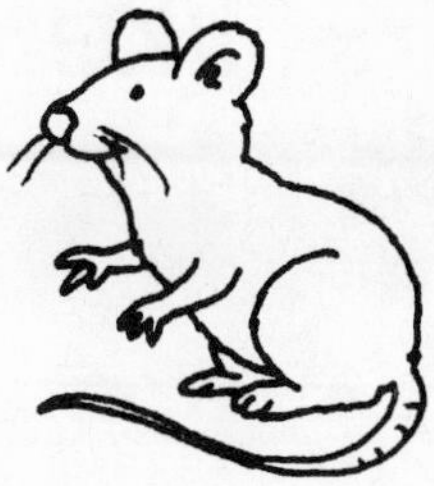

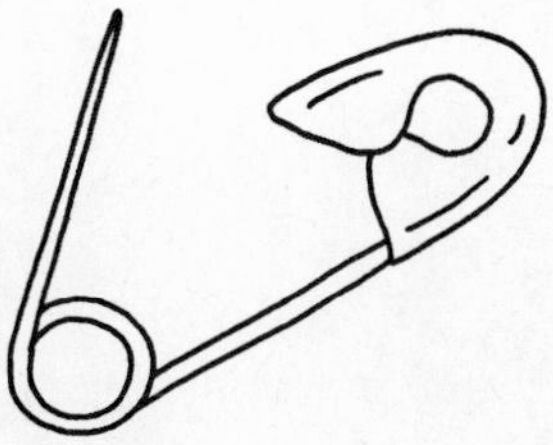

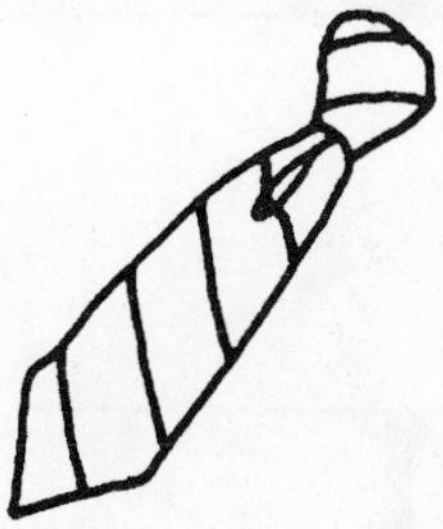

t

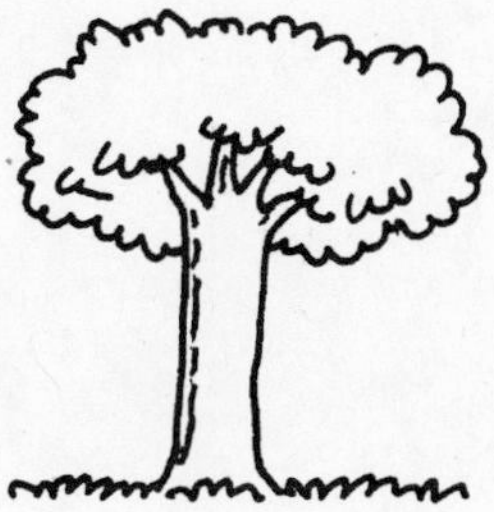

t

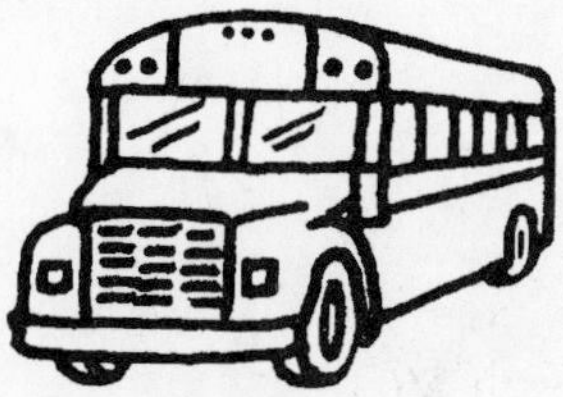

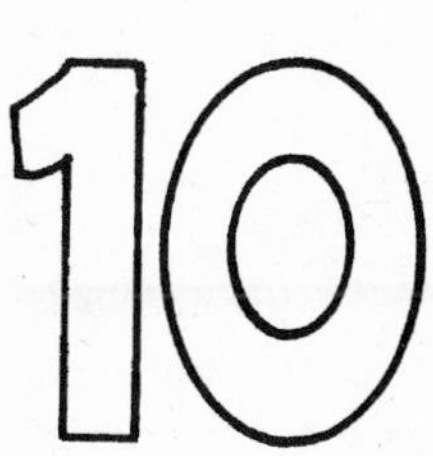

t 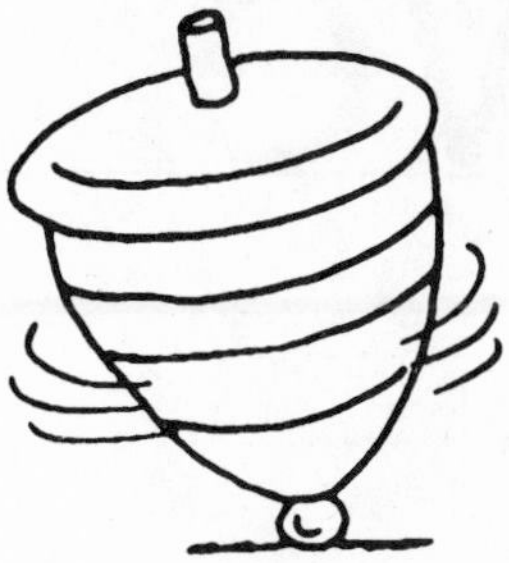 t

Phonics

Say the picture name. If the picture name begins with the /t/ sound, write *t* on the line.

Name ______________________________

can like we

can

like

we

High-Frequency Words

Read each word in the box. Then say the name of each picture. Write a word from the box that rhymes with each picture name.

Name ______________________

We like skates.

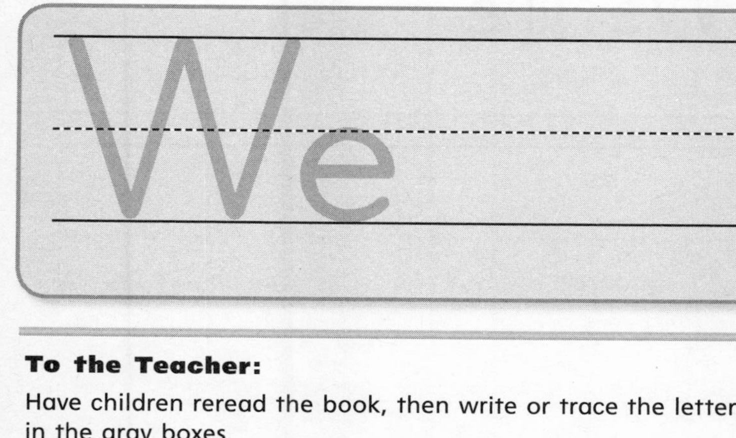

To the Teacher:
Have children reread the book, then write or trace the letters and words in the gray boxes.

We Like

We like  trucks.

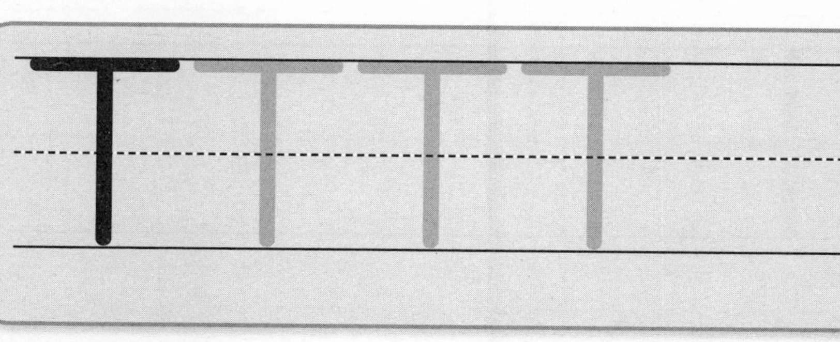

We like  .
trains

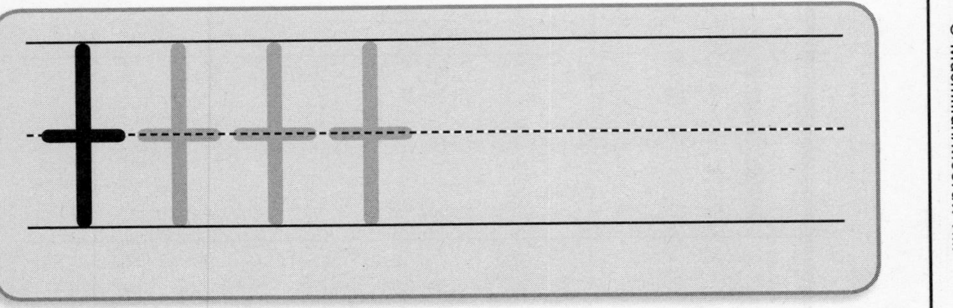

We like  .
tricycles

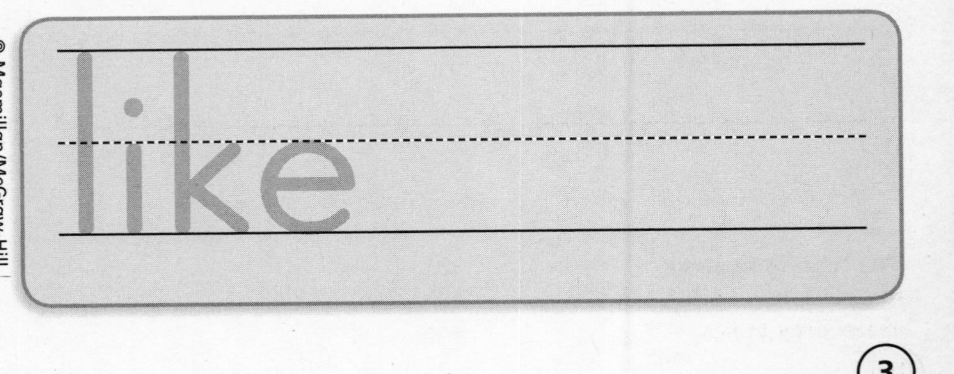

Name ____________________

We like a !
pie

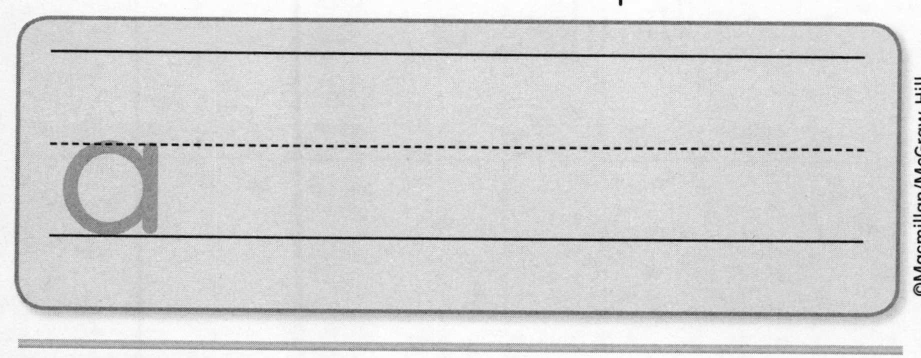

To the Teacher:

Have children reread the book, then write or trace the letters and words in the gray boxes.

We Like

I like a  .
nut

N N N N

I like a .

sandwich

nnn

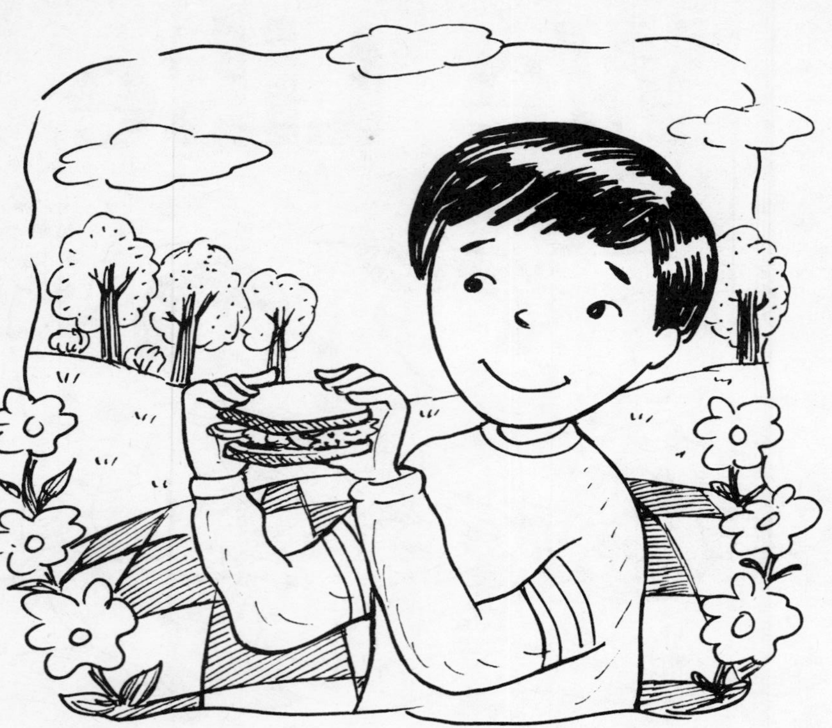

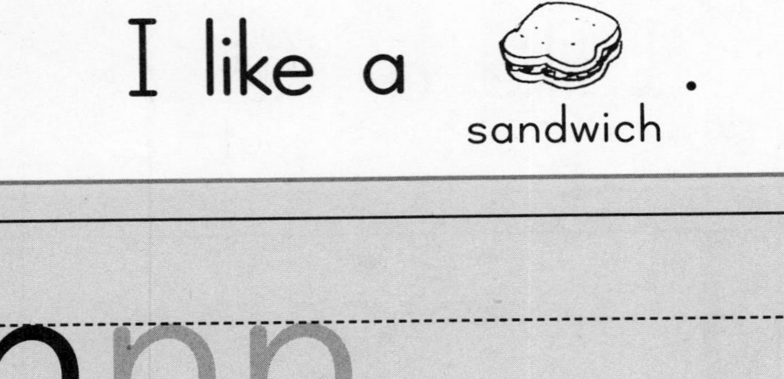

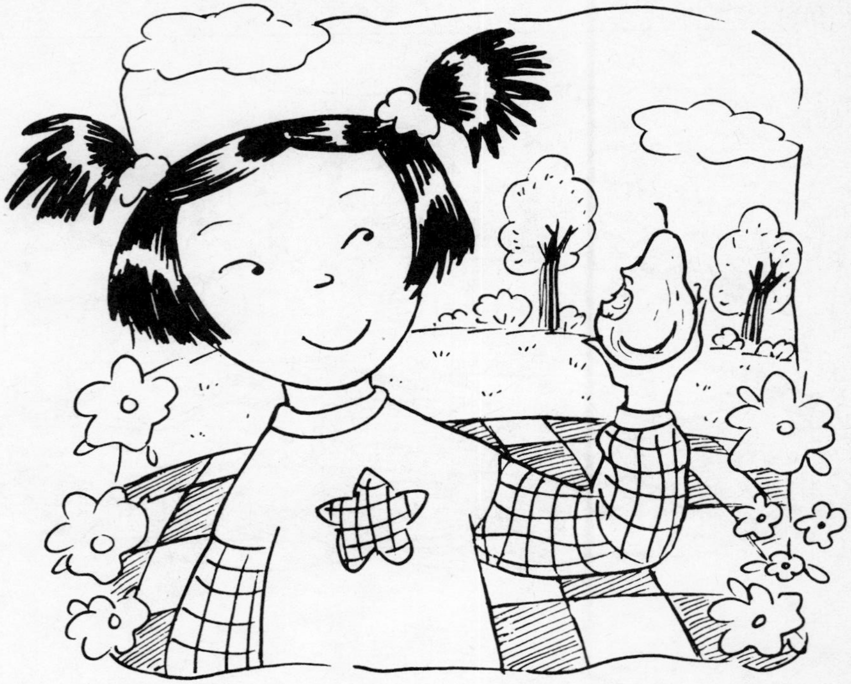

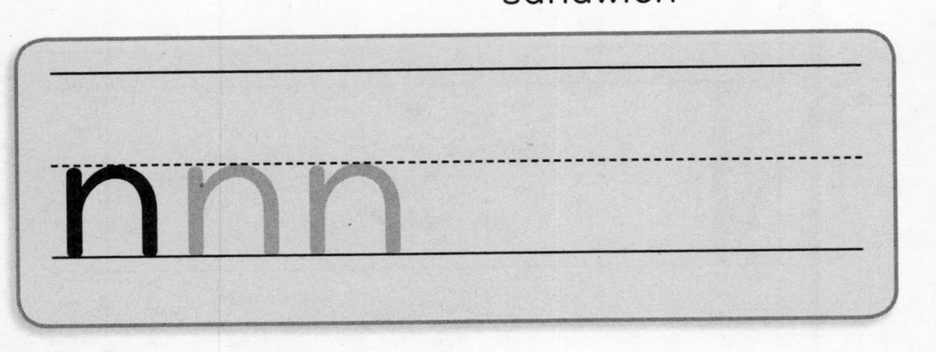

I like a .

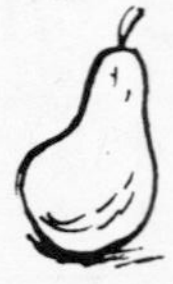

pear

like

Name ______________________________

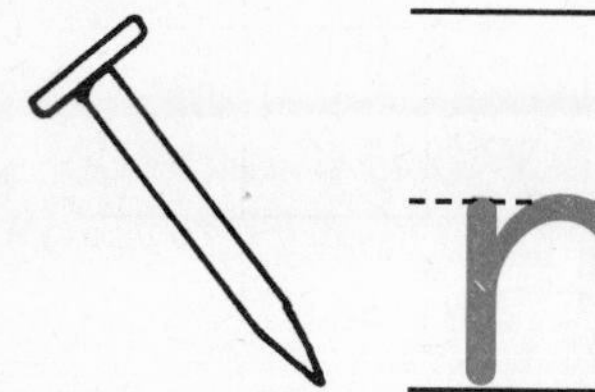 n 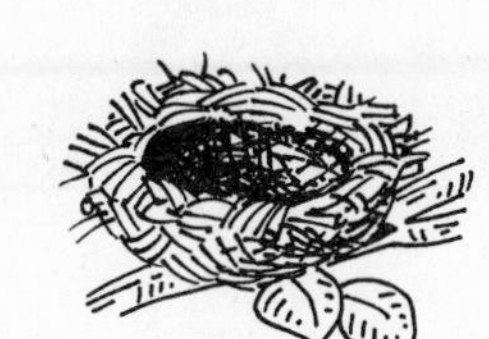  n 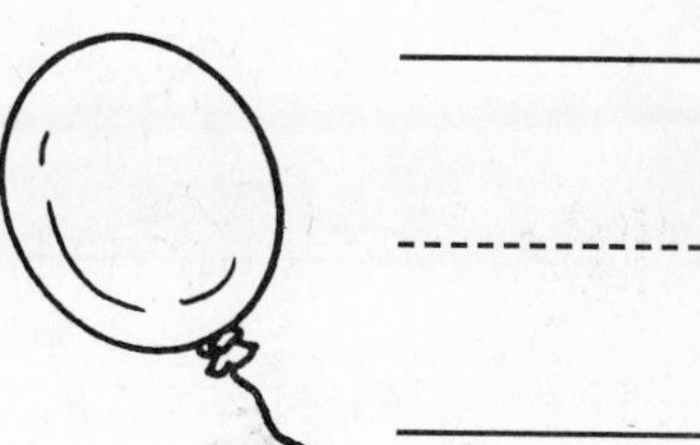

 n   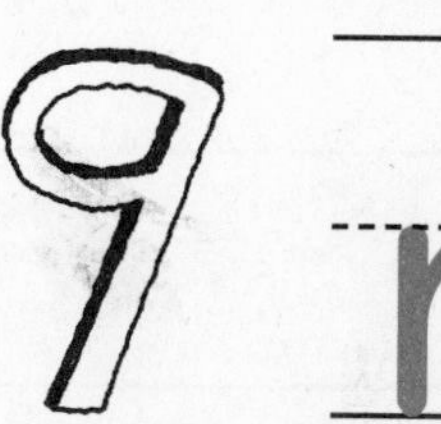 n

N N N

n n n

Phonics

 Say the picture names. If the picture begins with the /n/ sound, write *n* on the line.

 Trace and write the letter *Nn*.

Name ______________________________

a a

I I

can can

we we

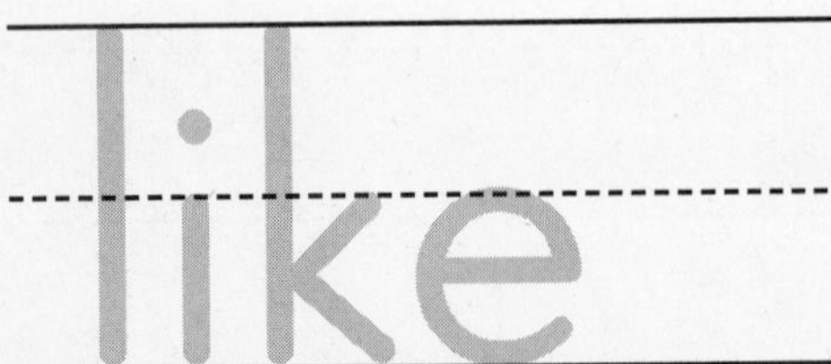

like like

High-Frequency Words

Say and trace the word *a*. Then write the word. Then build the word with your Letter Cards. Repeat with the words *I*, *can*, *we*, and *like*.

Name ____________________

I like a nest!

To the Teacher:

Have children reread the book, then write or trace the letters and words in the gray boxes.

I Like

I like a  nut.

I like a 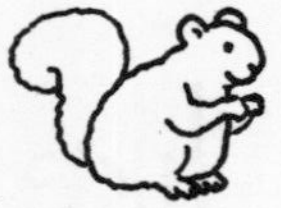 .

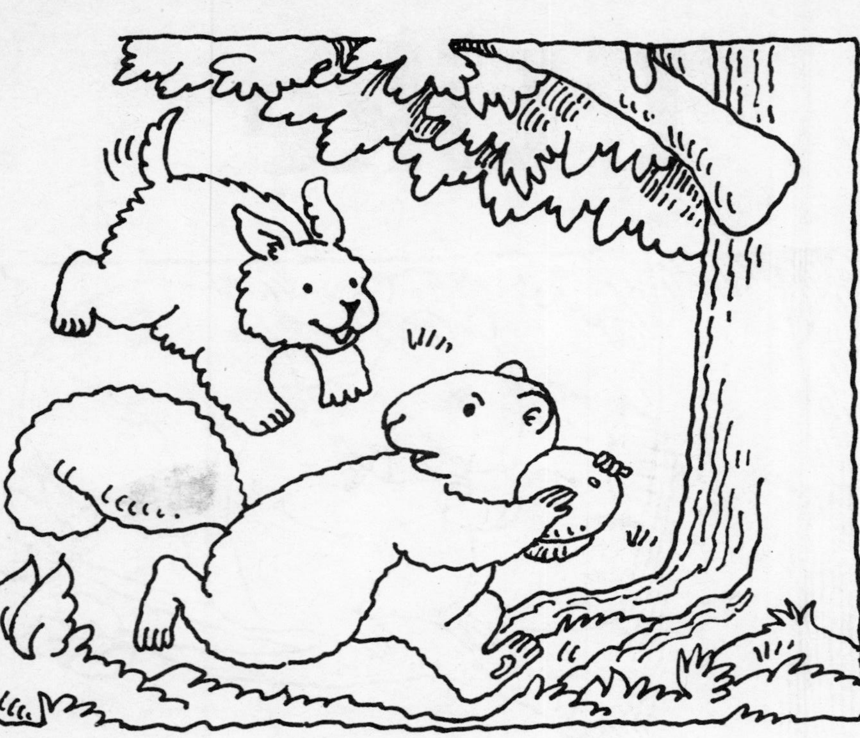

squirrel

nnn

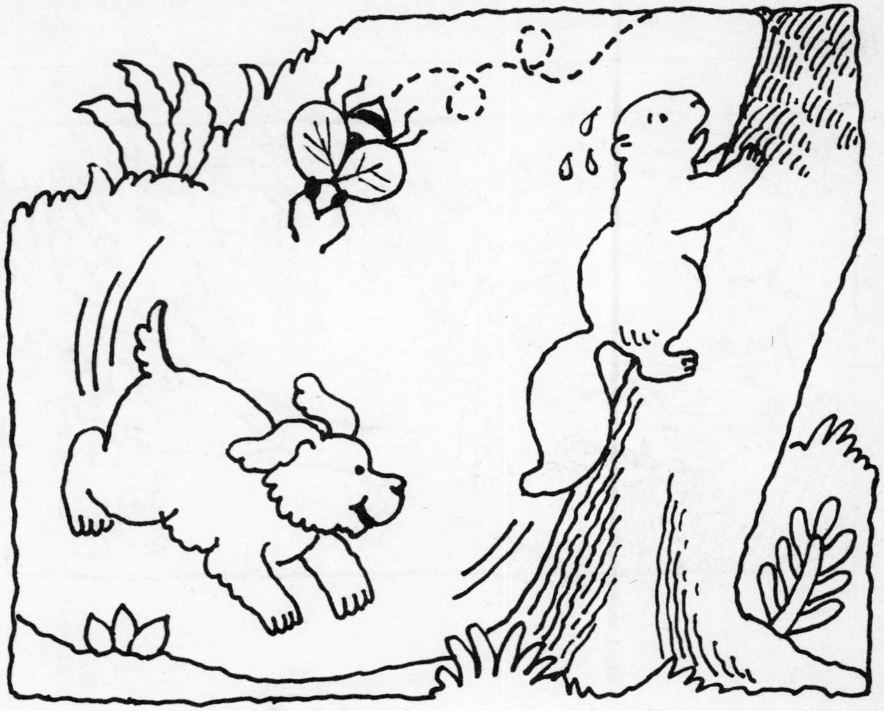

I like a 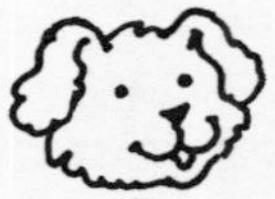 .

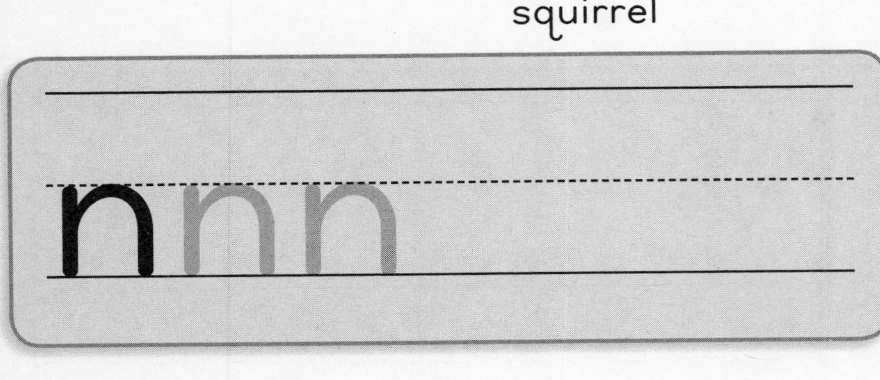

puppy

a

Name ______________________________

the dinner

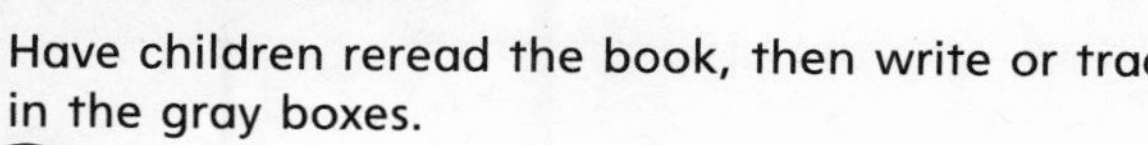

To the Teacher:
Have children reread the book, then write or trace the letters and words in the gray boxes.

The Cat

the can

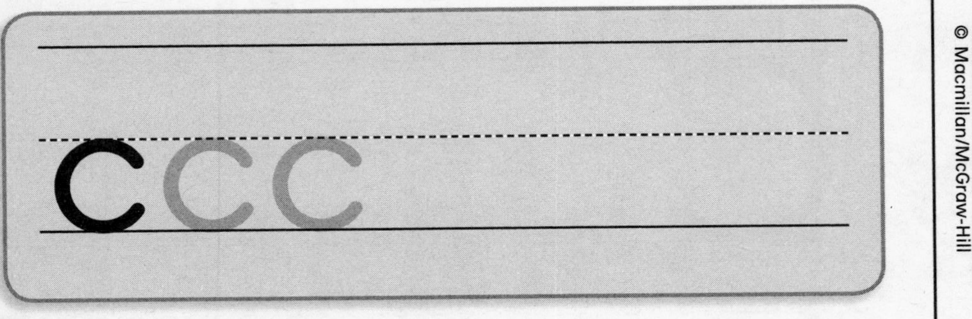

the bowl

Name

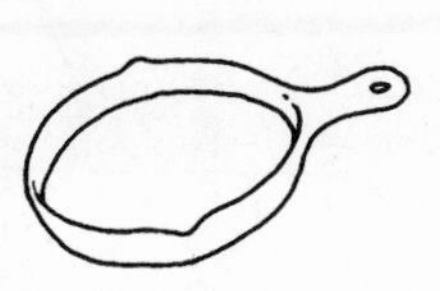
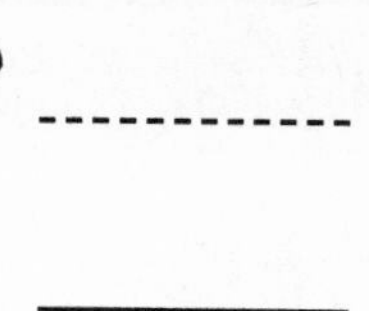

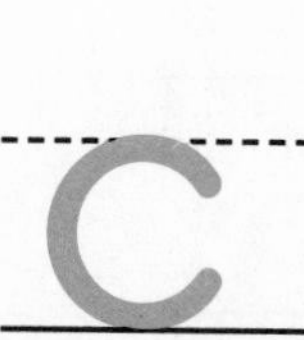

C C C

c c c

Phonics

 Say the picture name. If the picture name begins with the /k/ sound, write *c* on the line.

 Trace, and then write, *C* and *c* three more times.

Write

Name ___________________________

the the

like like

we we

can can

I I

High-Frequency Words

Say and trace the word *the*. Write the word. Then build the word with your Letter Cards. Repeat with the words *like*, *we*, *can*, and *I*.

Name ____________________

I like the rain.

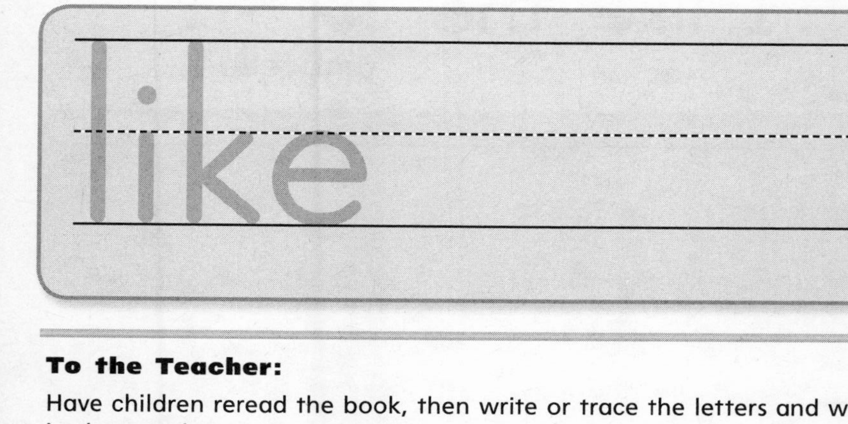

To the Teacher:

Have children reread the book, then write or trace the letters and words in the gray boxes.

The Rain

I like the  coat.

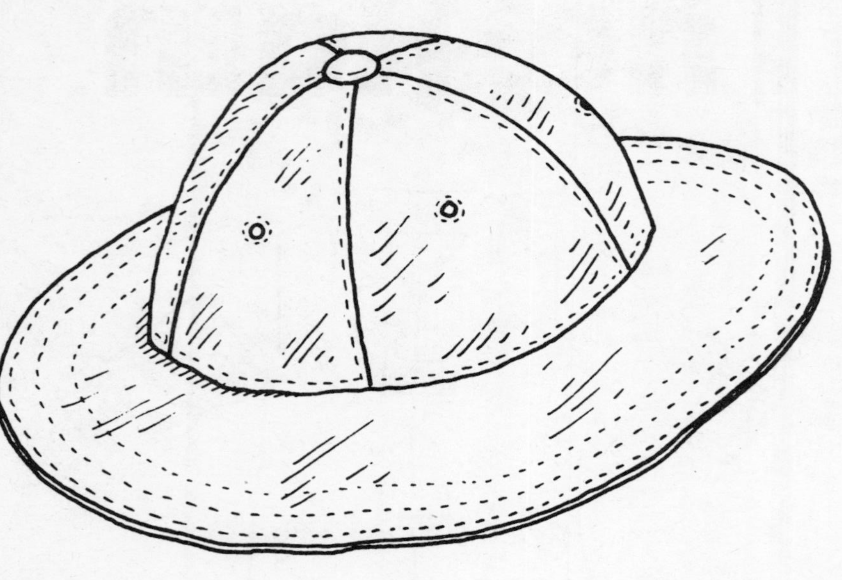

I like the  cap.

c c c

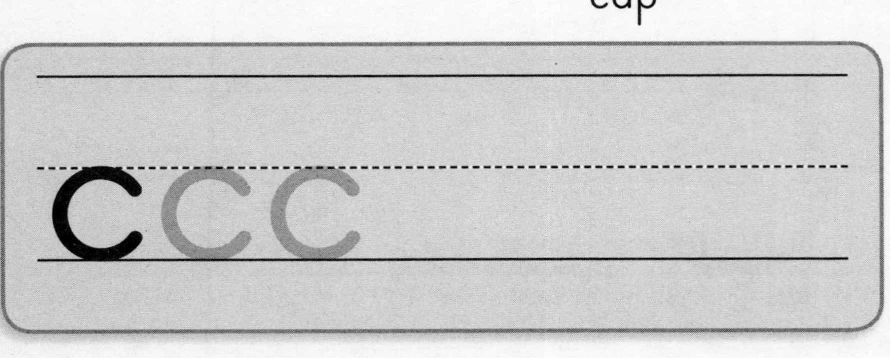

I like the  umbrella.

the

Name ______________________

We see!

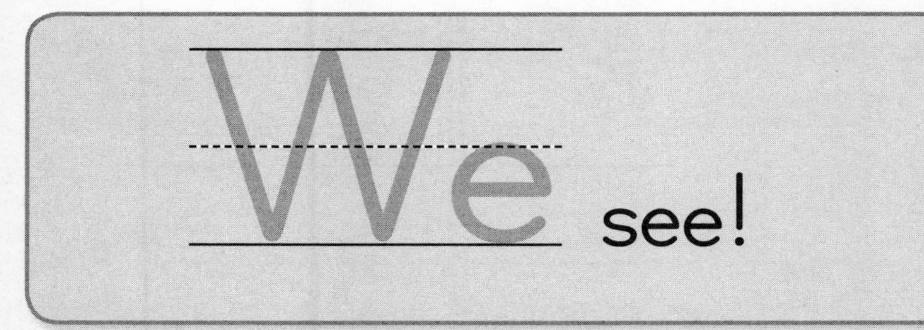

To the Teacher:
Have children reread the book, then write or trace the letters and words in the gray boxes.

We See

Frogs see.

FFFFF

 see.

Ducks

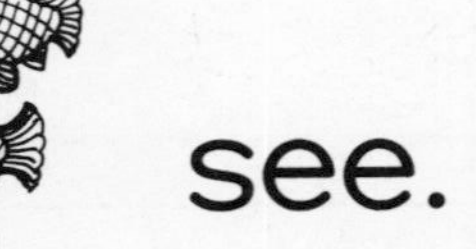 see.

Fish

Name ______________________________

 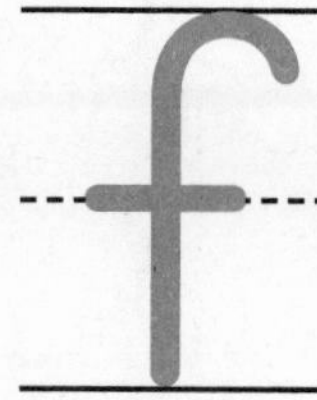  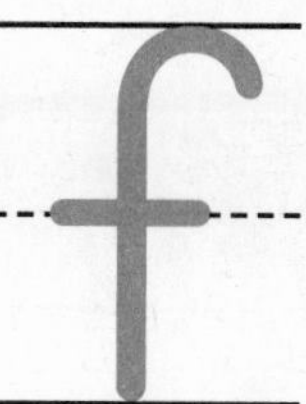 

 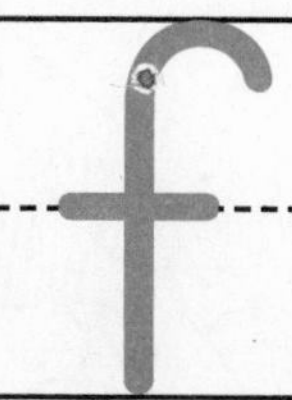  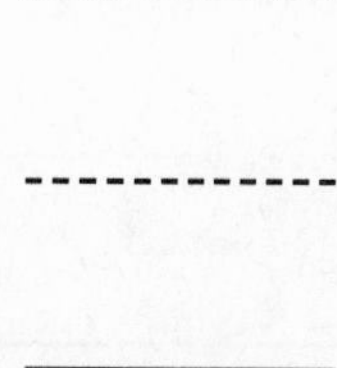  

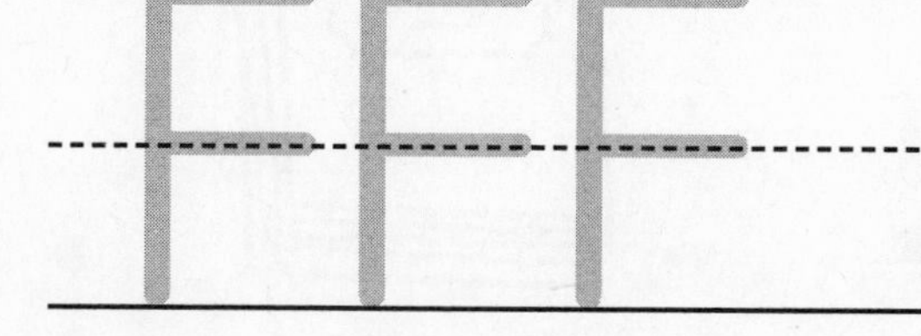

F F F

f f f

Phonics

 Say the picture name. If the picture name begins with the /f/ sound, write *f* on the line.

 Trace and write uppercase *F* and lowercase *f*.

Name ______________________________

I see a  .

I see a  .

I see a  .

I see a  .

High-Frequency Words

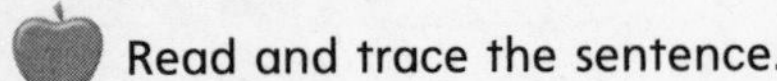
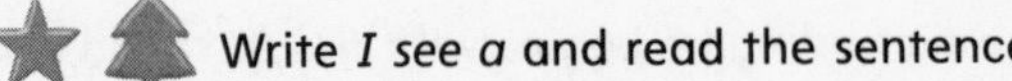
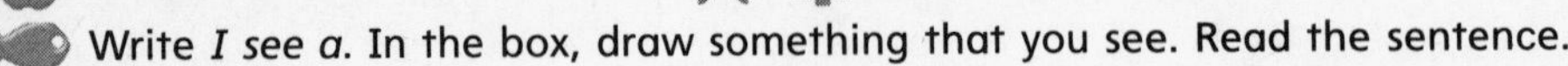

Read and trace the sentence. Write *I see a* and read the sentence.

Write *I see a*. In the box, draw something that you see. Read the sentence.

Name ______________________________

See the  duck .

To the Teacher:

Have children reread the book, then write or trace the letters and words in the gray boxes.

See

See the  feathers .

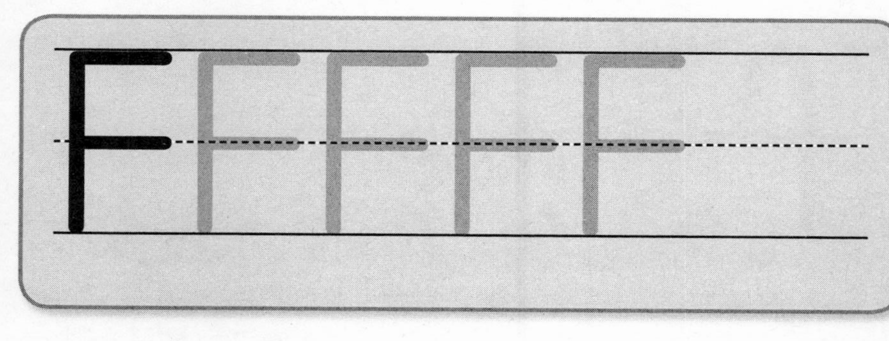

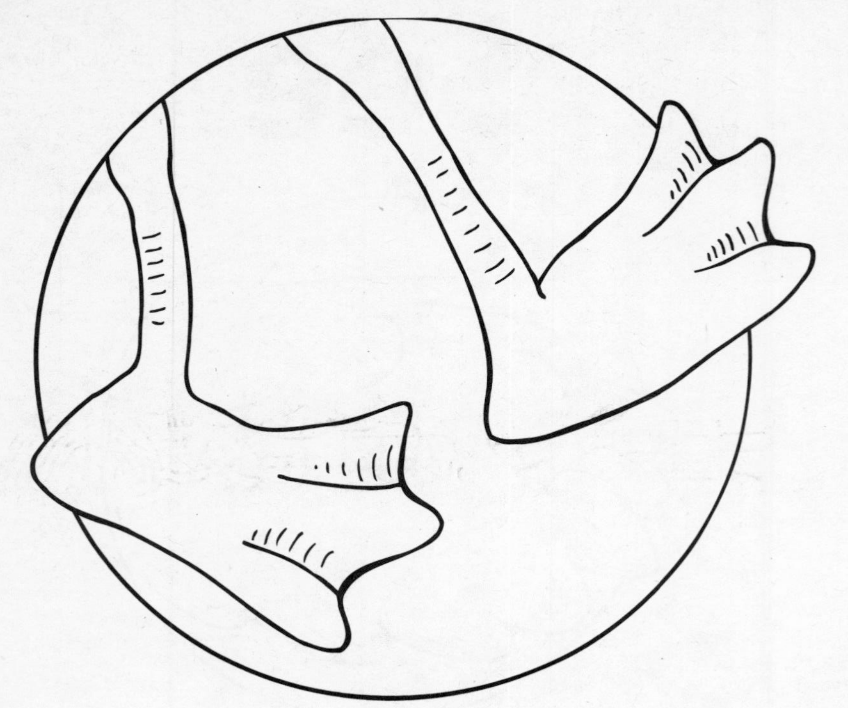

See the feet.

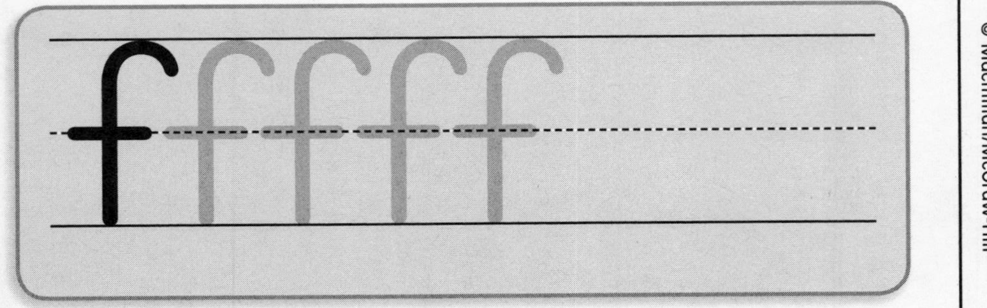

See the 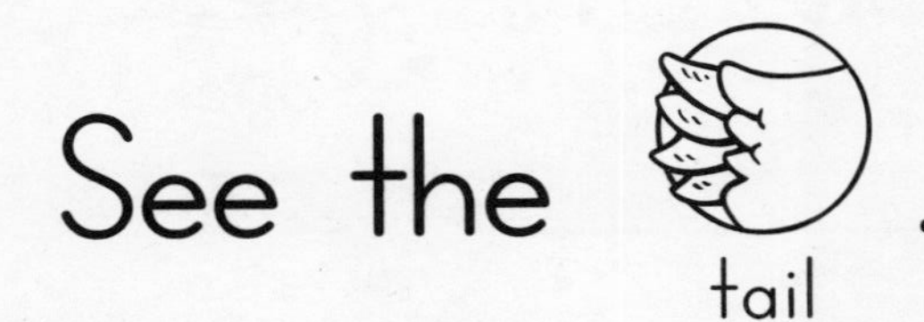 tail.

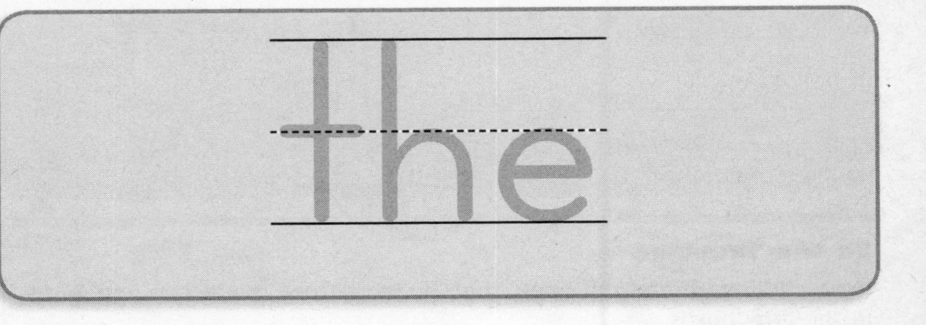

Name ______________________

We see cats.

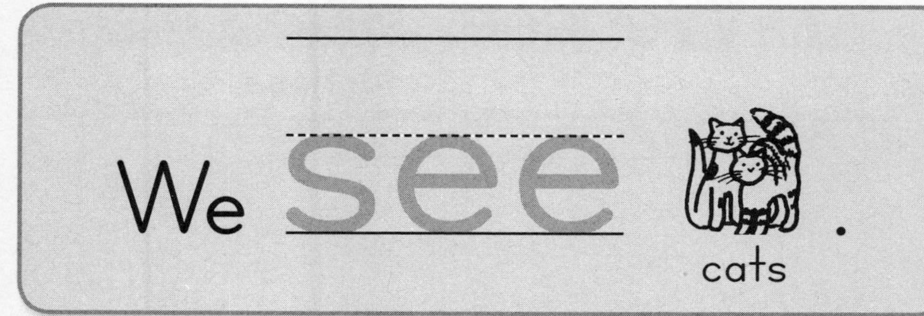

We see cats.

To the Teacher:

Have children reread the book, then write or trace the letters and words in the gray boxes.

We See

We see frogs.

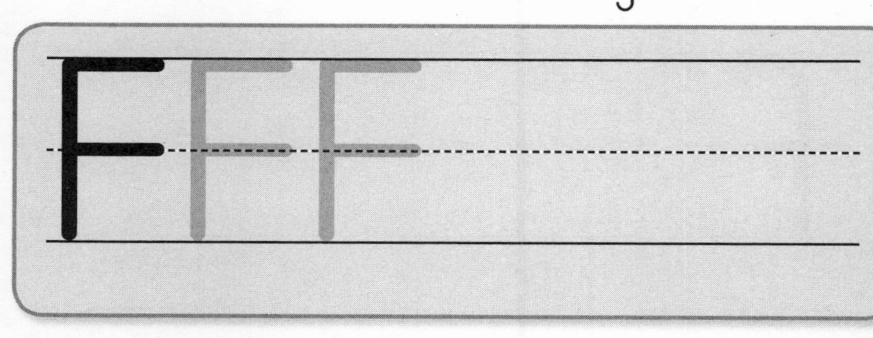

We see  .
mice

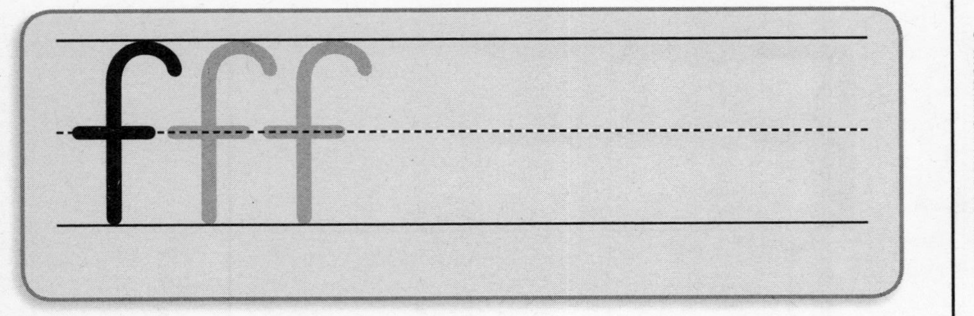

We see  .
turtles

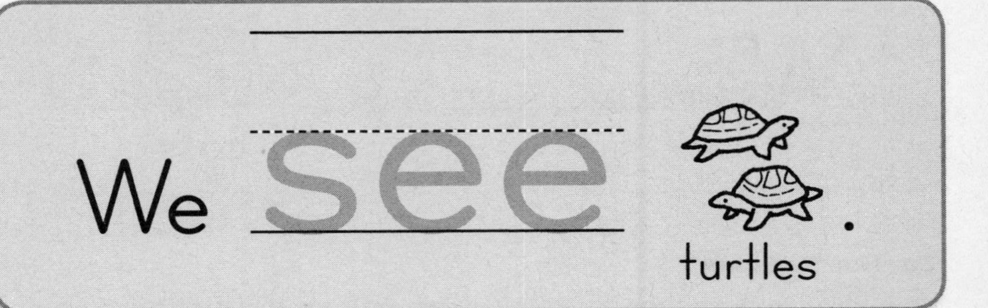

Name ______________________________

c

f

f

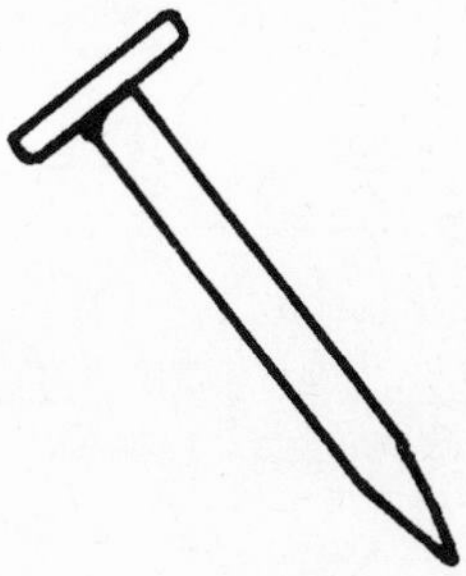

n

t

c

n

p

Phonics

Say the picture names. Write the letter that each picture name begins with.

Write

Name ______________________________

we we

like like

a a

the the

see see

High-Frequency Words

Say and trace the word *we*. Then write the word. Then build the word with your Letter Cards. Repeat with the words *like*, *a*, *the*, and *see*.

Name ______________________

I like presents.

I like presents.

To the Teacher:

Have children reread the book, then write or trace the letters and words in the gray boxes.

I Like

I like stars.

C C C C

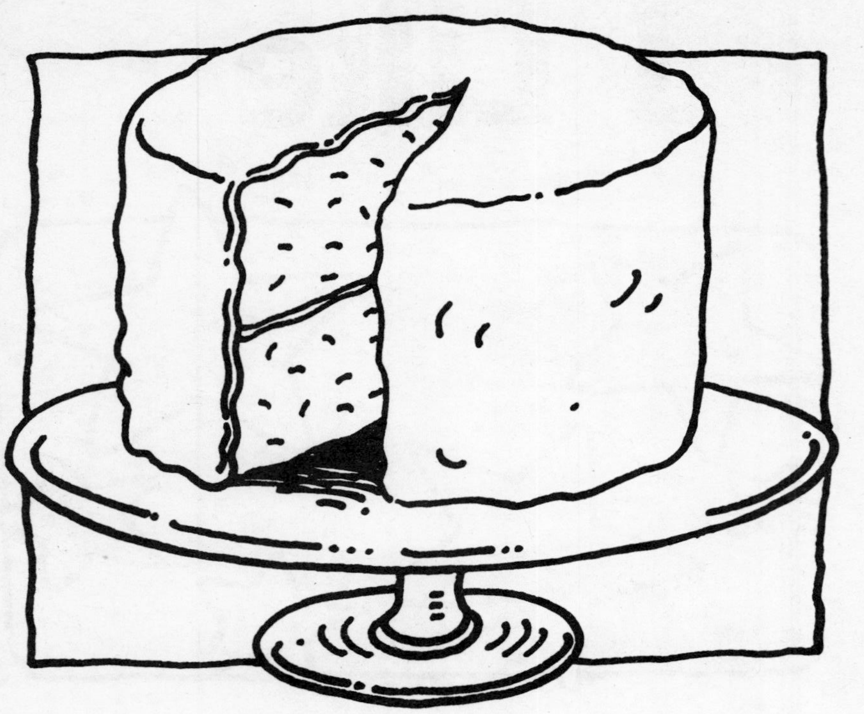

I like cake .

C C C C

I like candles .

Name ______________________

Go, horse, go!

Go, horse, go!

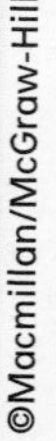

To the Teacher: Have children reread the book, then write or trace the letters and words in the gray boxes.

Go!

Go, ram, go!

MM

Go, lamb, go!

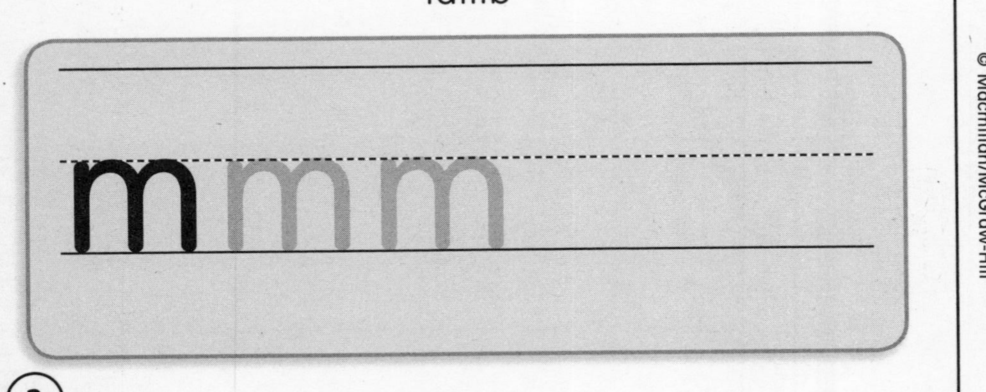

Go, cow, go!

Name ______________________________

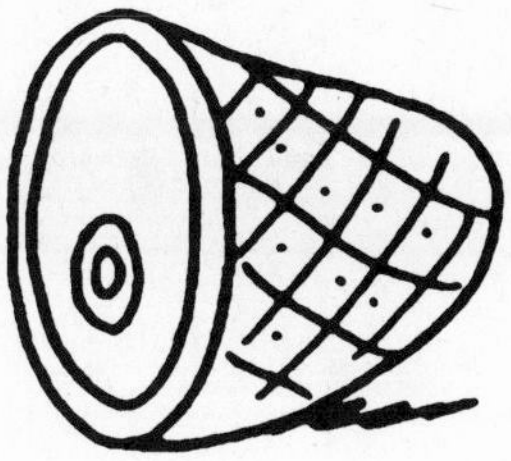

m 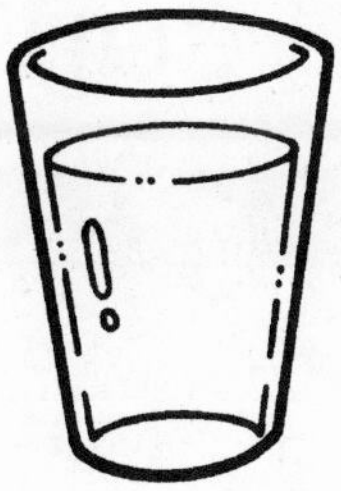 s

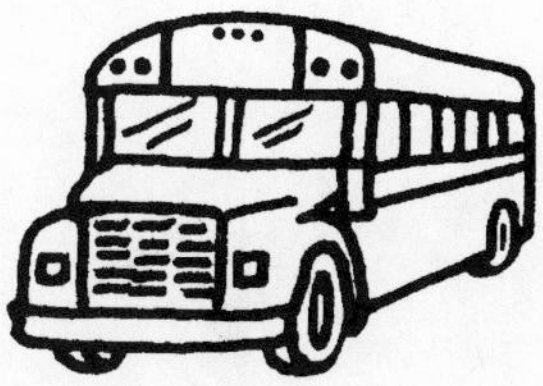

s 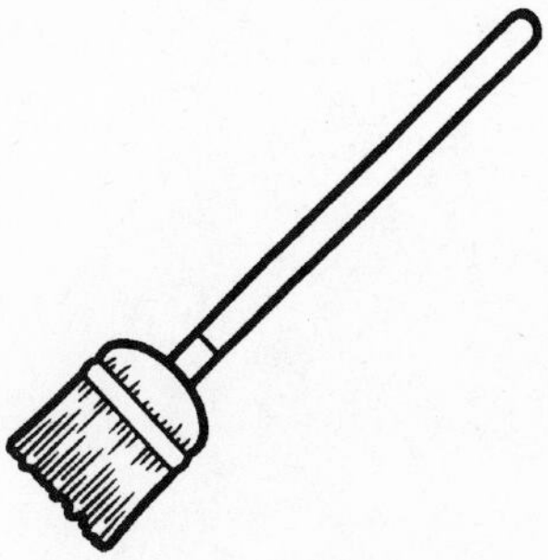 m

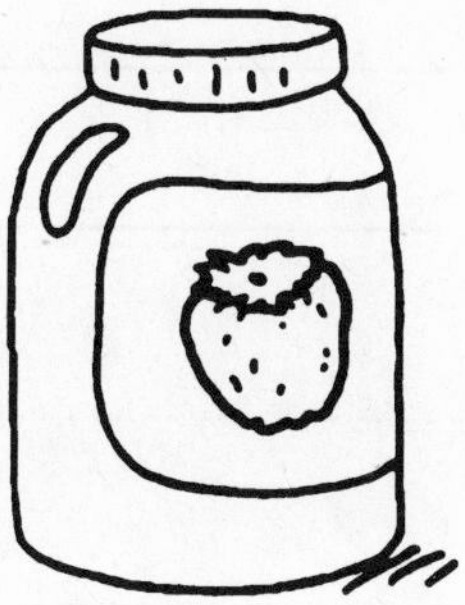

m 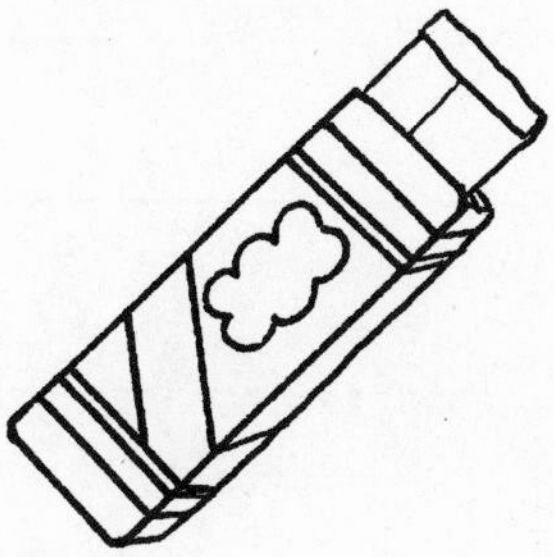 m

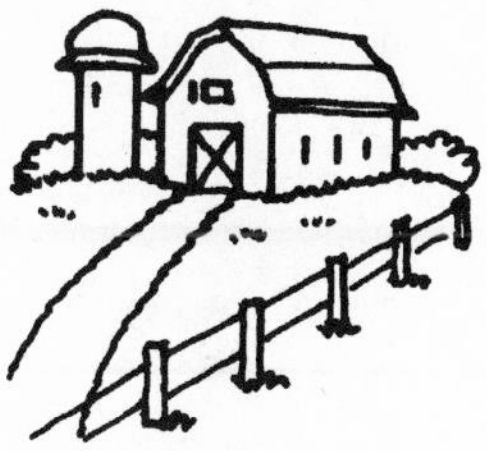

m 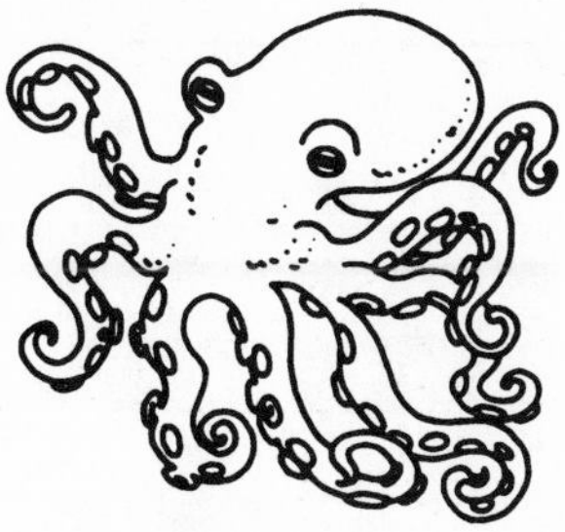 s

Phonics

Say the picture name. If the name ends with the /m/ sound, write *m* on the line. If the name ends with the /s/ sound, write *s* on the line.

Name ___________________________

I can go.

I can go.

I can go.

High-Frequency Words

Read the sentence. Think of somewhere you like to go and draw a picture of that place. Then trace and write the sentence *I can go*.

Name ______________________

We go!

To the Teacher:

Have children reread the book, then write or trace the letters and words in the gray boxes.

We Go

Zebras go.

S S S

Tigers go.

s s s

Elephants go.

Elephants go.

Name ______________________

I have a  mop.

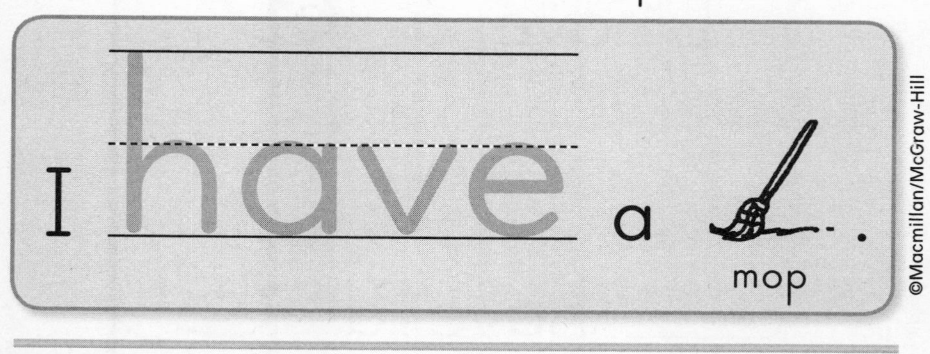

I have a mop.

To the Teacher:
Have children reread the book, then write or trace the letters and words in the gray boxes.

I Have

I have a  ship.

P P P

I have a whale.

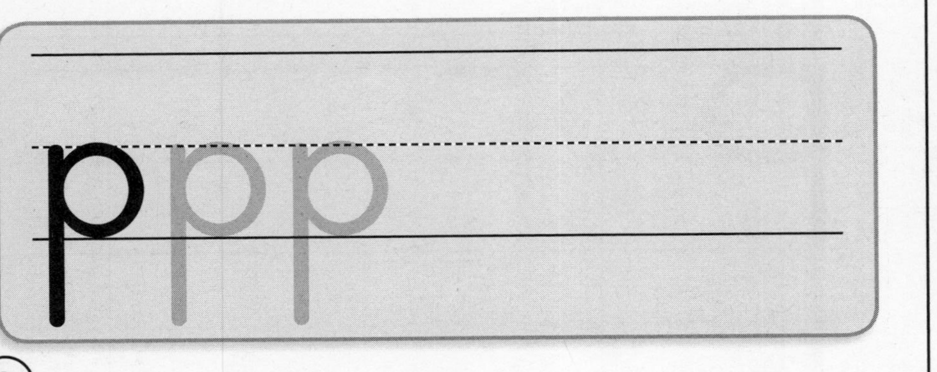

Name ___

n  t

t  p

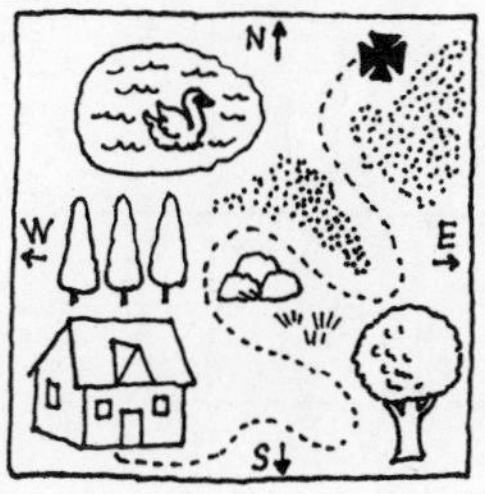

p  n

n  t

Phonics

Say the picture name. If the name ends with the /p/ sound, write *p* on the line. If the name ends with the /t/ sound, write *t* on the line. If the name ends with the /n/ sound, write *n* on the line.

Name ______________________________

have have

go go

see see

the the

like like

High-Frequency Words

Say and trace the word *have*. Then write the word. Build the word with your Letter Cards. Repeat with the words *go*, *see*, *the*, and *like*.

Name ____________________

I have a castle !

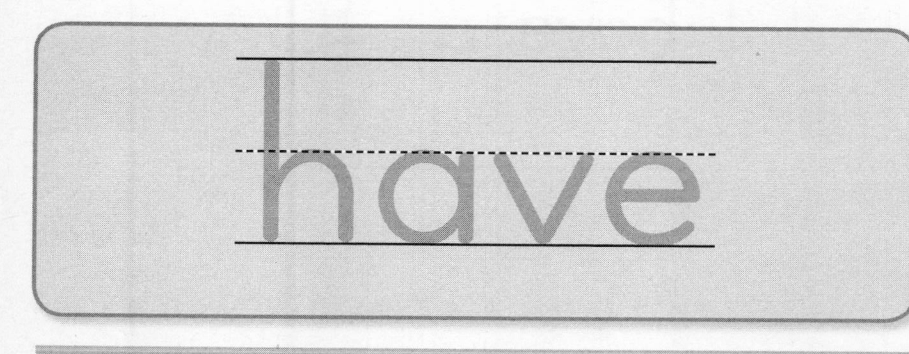

To the Teacher:

Have children reread the book, then write or trace the letters and words in the gray boxes.

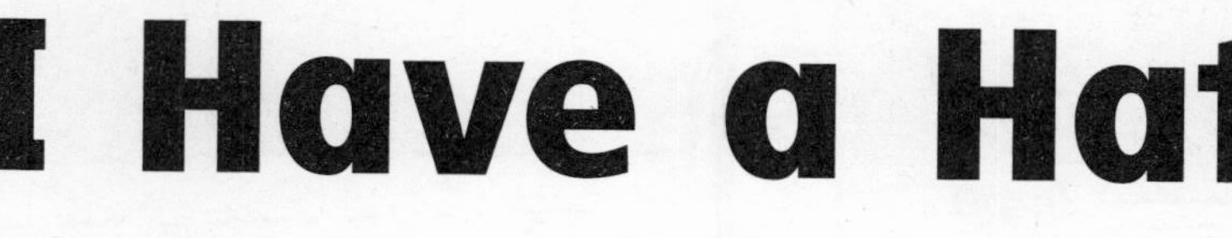

I Have a Hat

I have a  hat .

T T T

I have a  fan.

t

I have a  pot.

have

Name ______________________

I can play!

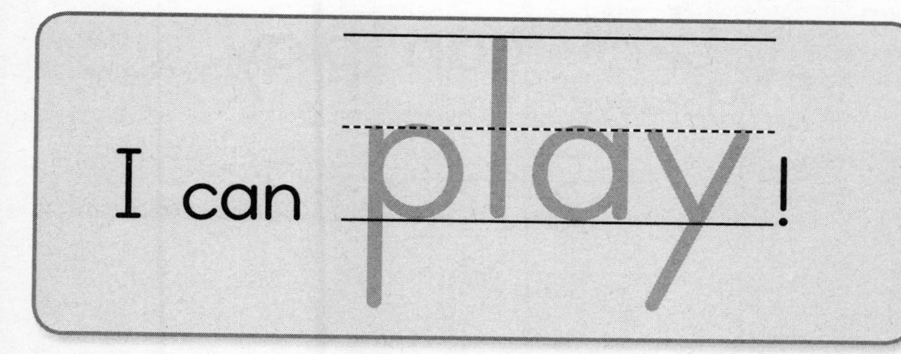

To the Teacher:
Have children reread the book, then write or trace the letters and words in the gray boxes.

Horses can play.

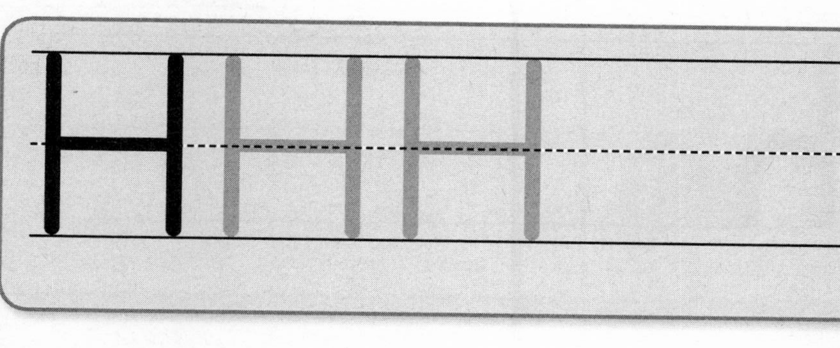

Hippos can play.

hhh

Monkeys can play.

can

Name

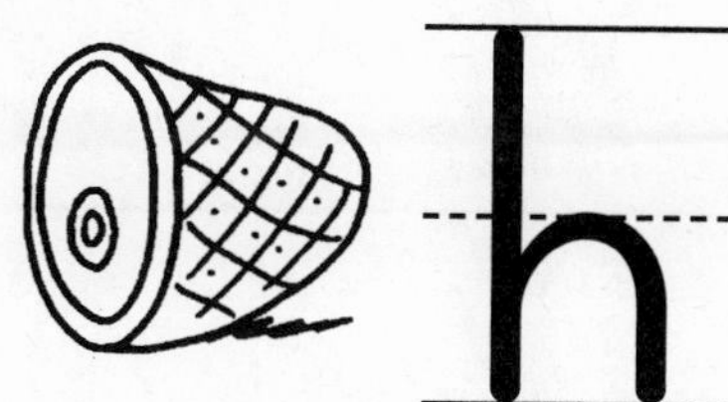
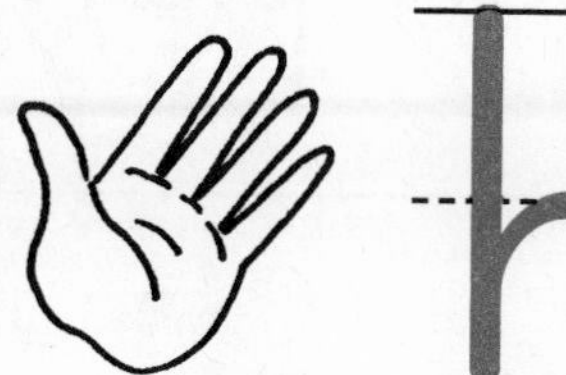
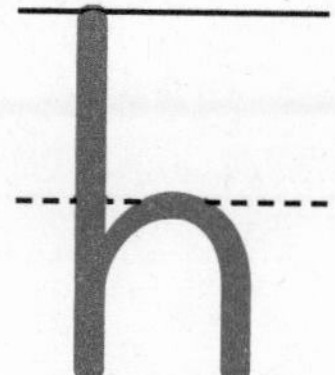
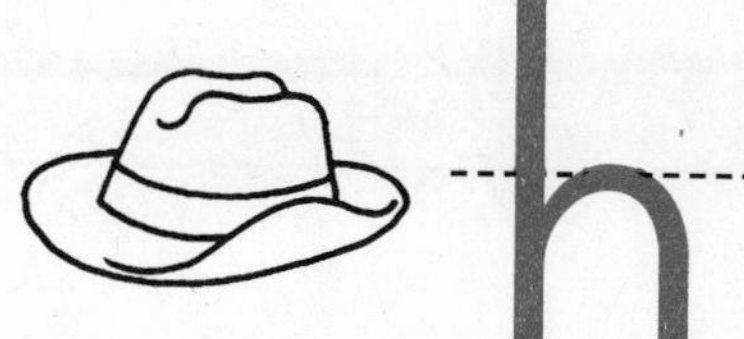

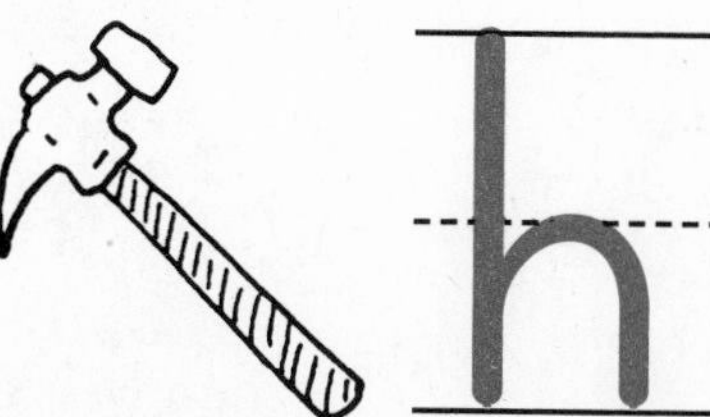
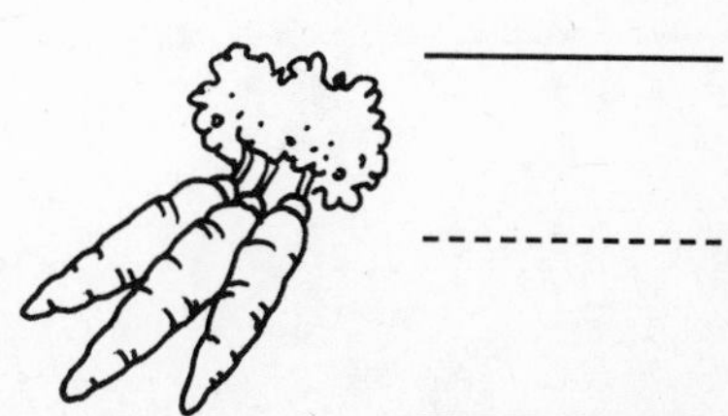

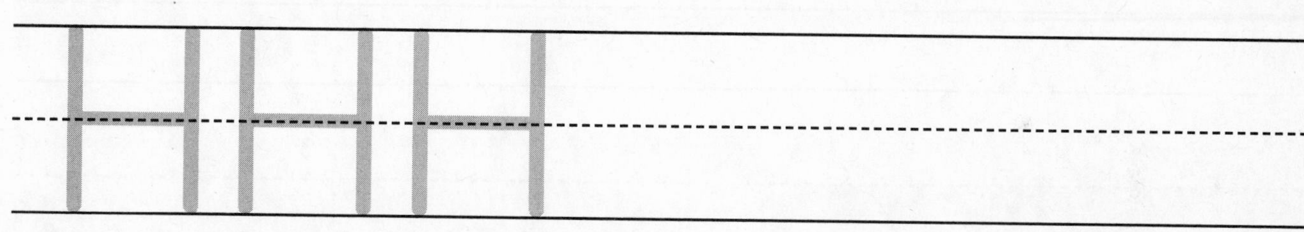

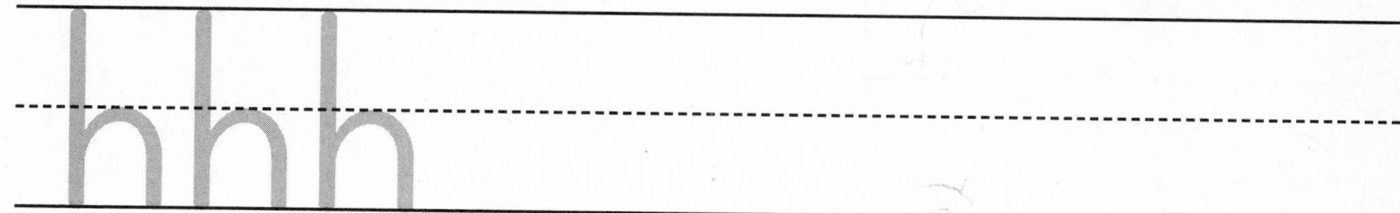

Phonics

 Say the picture name. If the name begins with the /h/ sound, write *h* on the line.

 Trace and write the letter *Hh*.

Name ______________________________

I can play.

I can play.

High-Frequency Words

Read the sentence. Think of something you like to play and draw a picture of yourself playing. Then trace and write the sentence *I can play.*

Name ____________________

I play a  drum .

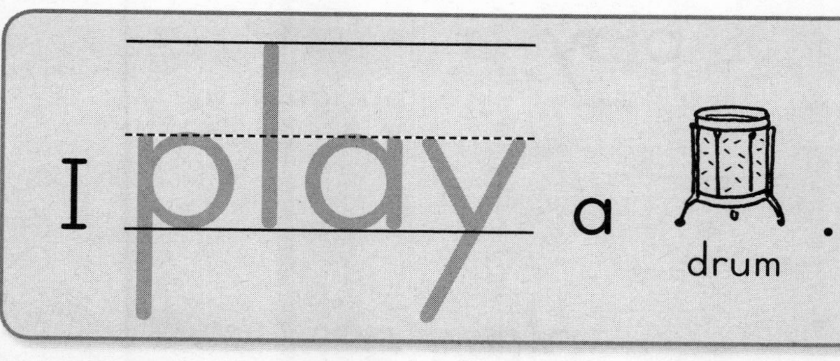

To the Teacher:
Have children reread the book, then write or trace the letters and words in the gray boxes.

I Play

I play a horn .

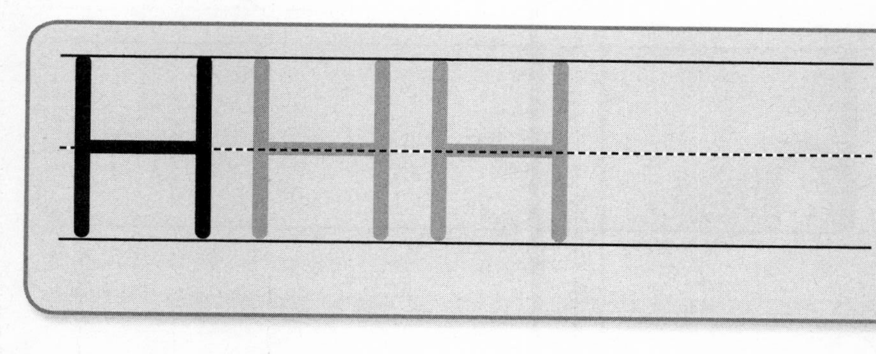

I play a  harp.

h h h

I play a  harmonica.

I play a  harmonica.

Name ______________________

We like to play!

to

To the Teacher:

Have children reread the book, then write or trace the letters and words in the gray boxes.

We Like

We like to play.

A A A

We like to [jump].

We like to [run].

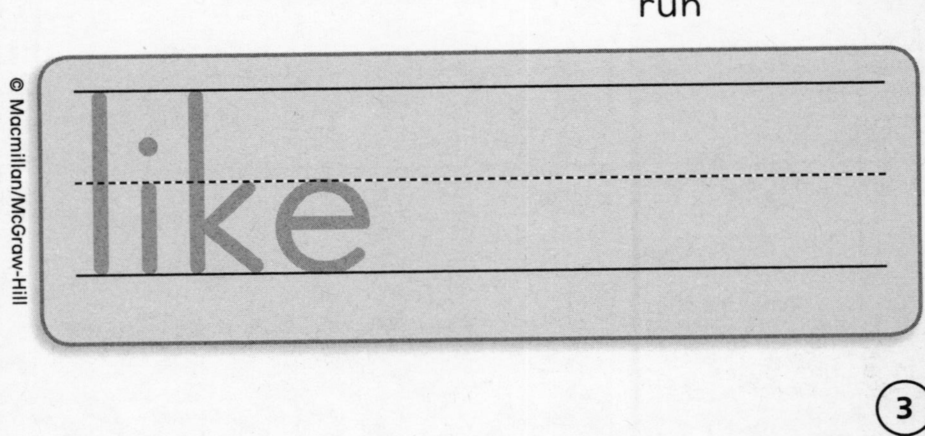

Name ________________________________

h	a	t
c	a	t
f	a	n

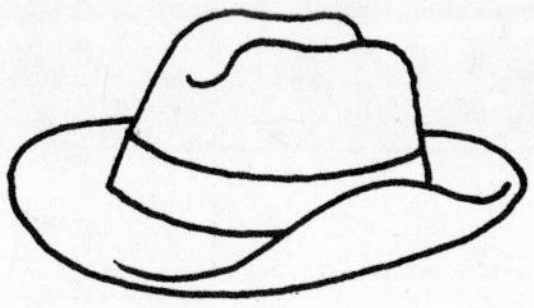

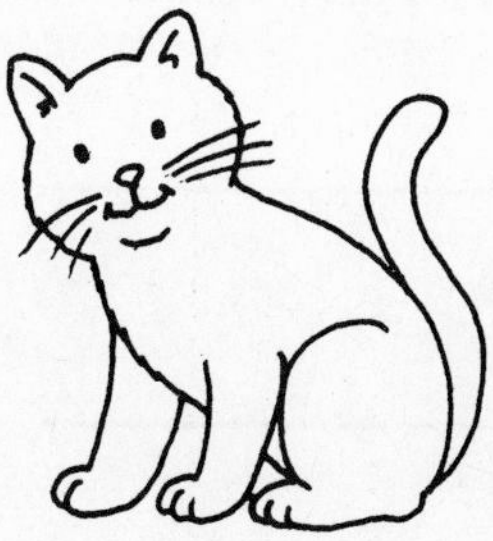

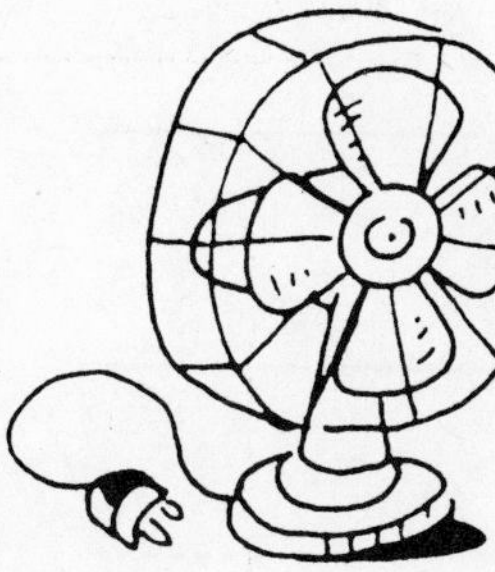

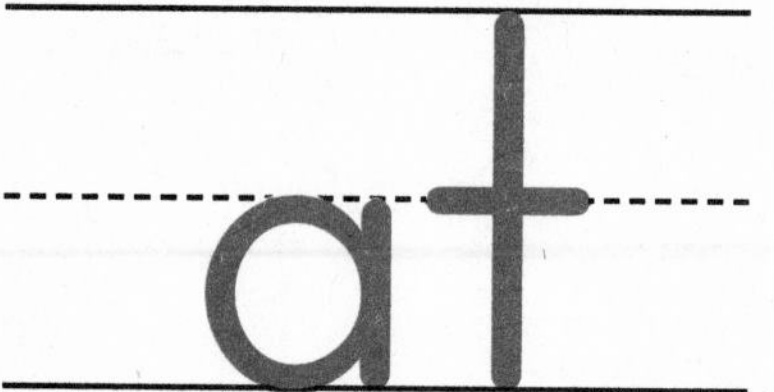

Phonics

 Say the picture names. Then trace the letters. Fill in the missing letter *a*.

 Dictation: Write the following words: *a, at, an.*

Name ____________________

to

play

have

go

see

High-Frequency Words

Say and trace the word *to*. Then write the word. Then build the word with your Letter Cards. Repeat with the words *play*, *have*, *go*, and *see*.

Name ____________________

I have to nap.

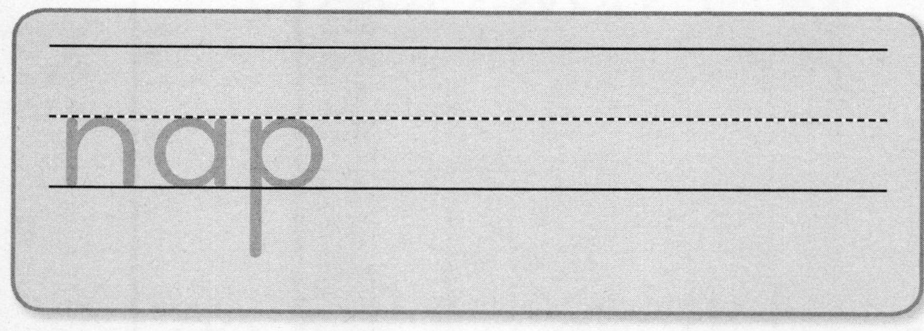

To the Teacher:

Have children reread the book, then write or trace the letters and words in the gray boxes.

Sam

I have to tap.

A A A

I have to  eat.

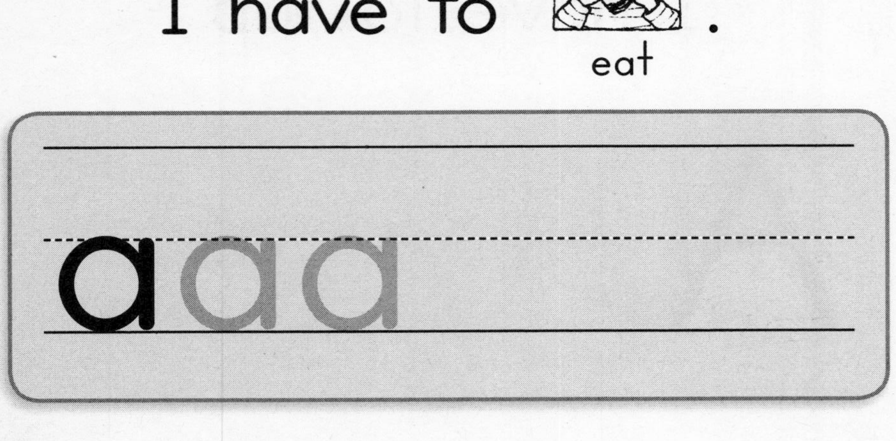

a a a

I have to go.

I have to go.

Name ______________________________

Dan is a dad.

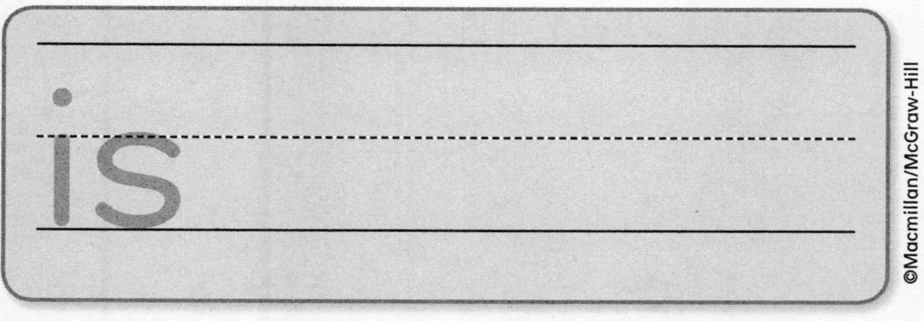

To the Teacher:
Have children reread the book, then write or trace the letters and words in the gray boxes.

Dan

Dan is a cat.

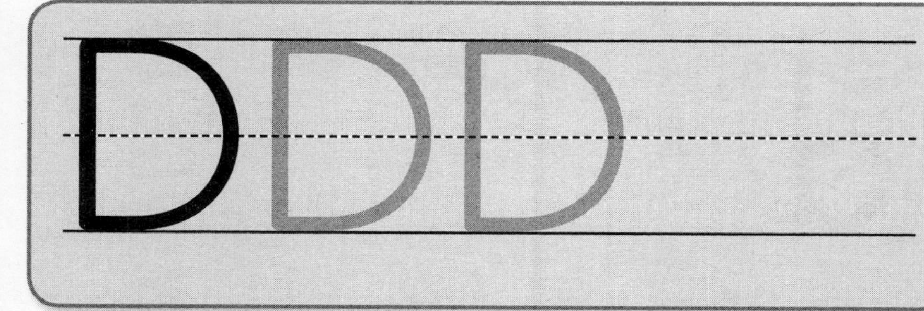

Dan is a bird.

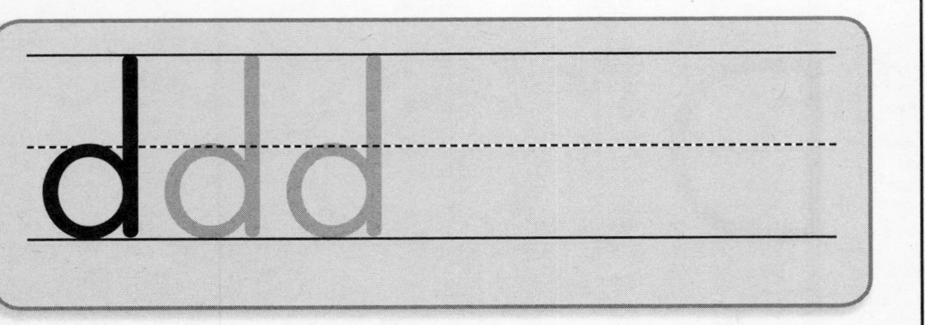

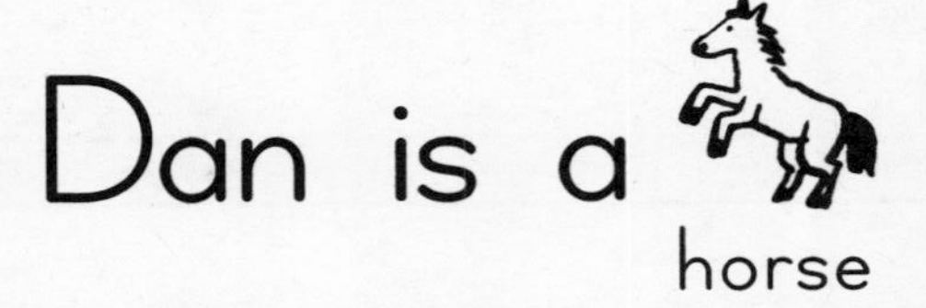

Dan is a horse.

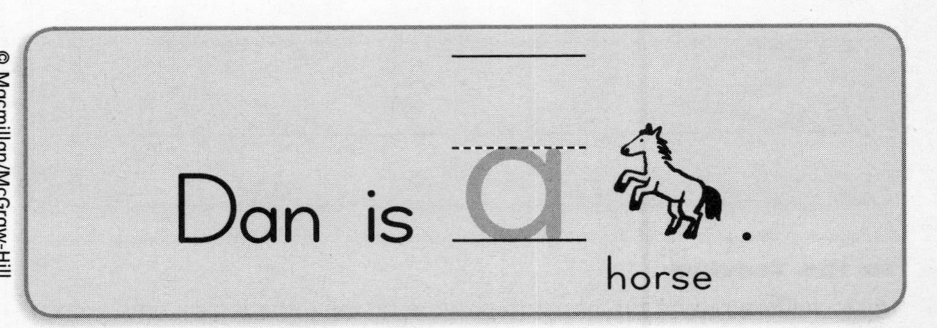

Name ______________________

 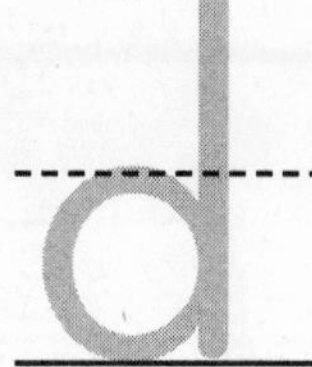  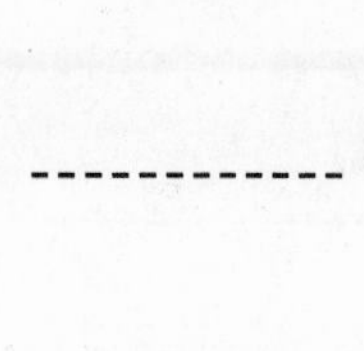 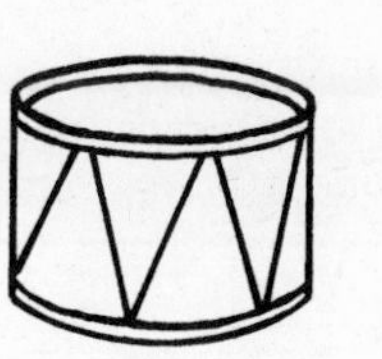 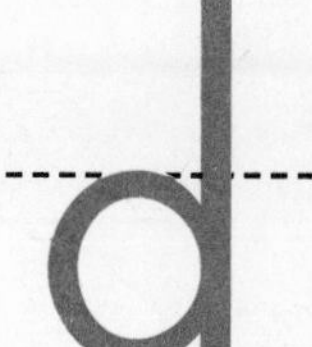

 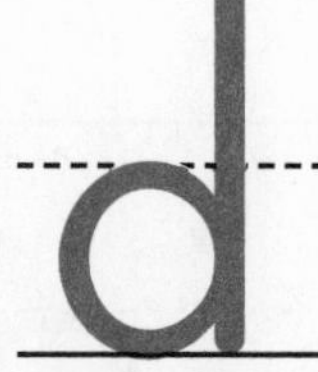  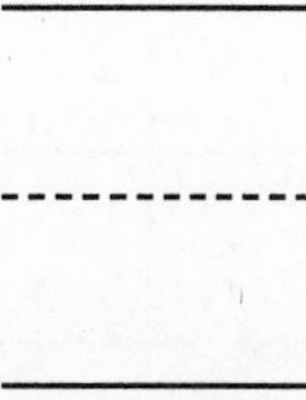 

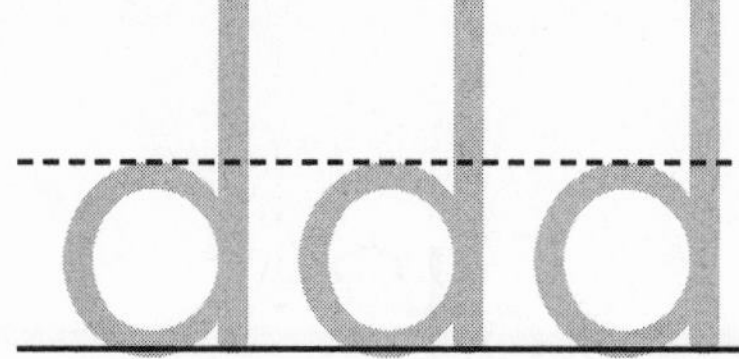

Phonics

 Say the picture names. If the picture name begins with the /d/ sound, write *d* on the line.

 Trace and write the letter *Dd*.

Write

Name ______________________

we	to	see	is

1. we
2. to
3. see
4. is

1. Dan is a cat.
2. Do you see the cat?

High-Frequency Words

 Read the words in the box. Write one word on each line.

 Use a word from the box to finish each sentence.

Name ____________________

Ann is like Dad.

To the Teacher:
Have children reread the book, then write or trace the letters and words in the gray boxes.

Dad

Sam is like Dad.

D D D

Pam is like Dad.

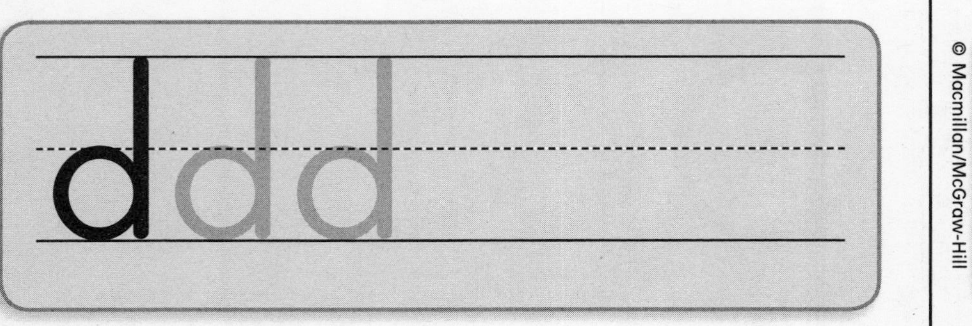

dad

Dan is like Dad.

Dad

Name ____________________

We have to nap.

To the Teacher:
Have children reread the book, then write or trace the letters and words in the gray boxes.

We Have

We have to pat.

A A A

We have to tap.

We have to  .
read

Name ____________________

 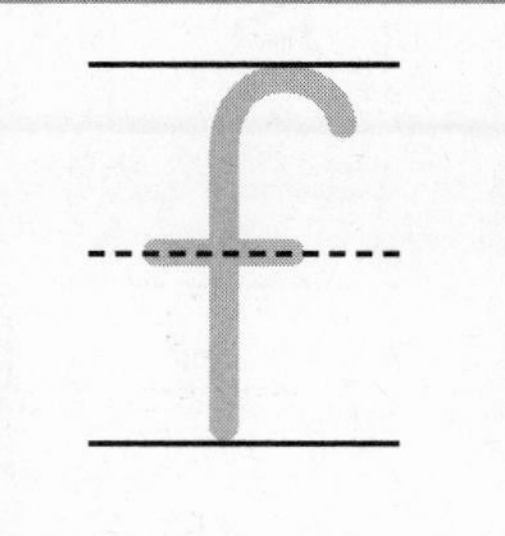  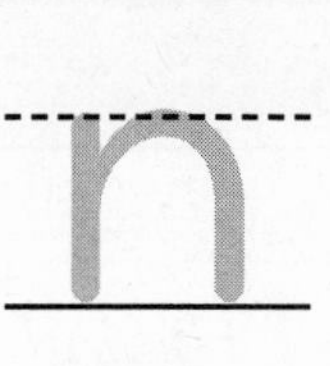

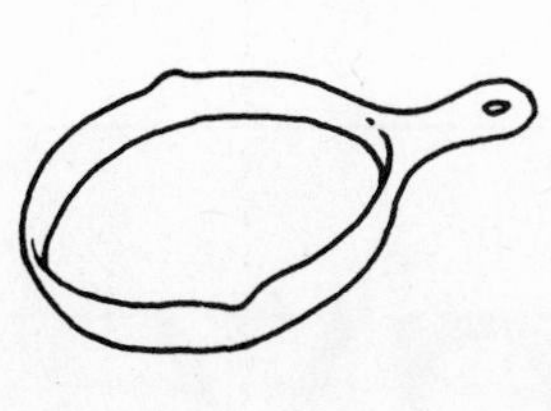 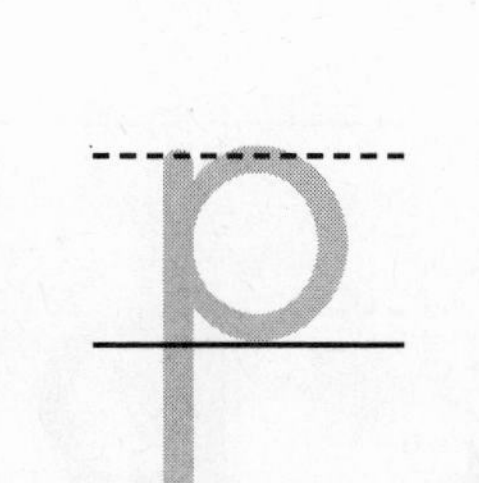  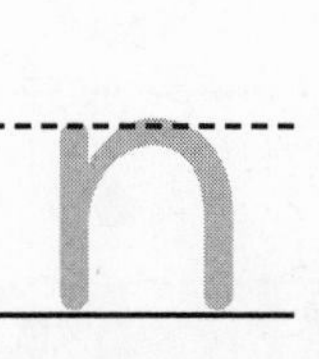

   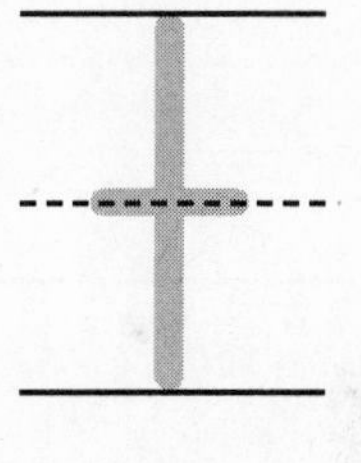

 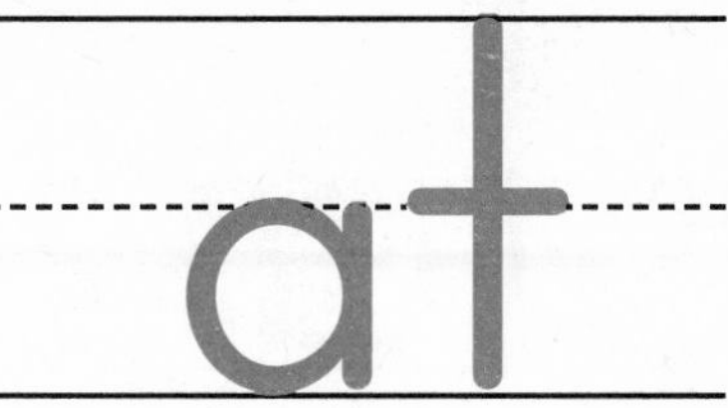 

Phonics

 Say the picture names. Trace the letters. Fill in the missing letter *a*.

 Dictation: Write the following words: *an*, *at*, *bat*.

Write

Name ______________________________

go	to	is	play

1. go
2. to
3. is
4. play

1. I go to [school].
2. I like to play.

High-Frequency Words

 Read the words in the box. Write one word on each line.

 Choose a word from the box to finish each sentence. Read the sentence.

Name ____________________

Go, go, go!

To the Teacher:
Have children reread the book, then write or trace the letters and words in the gray boxes.

Go, Go, Go!

Go, Dan.

Go, Pam.

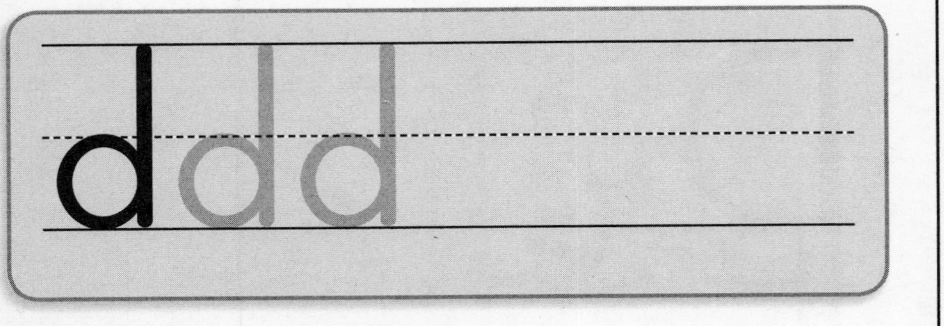
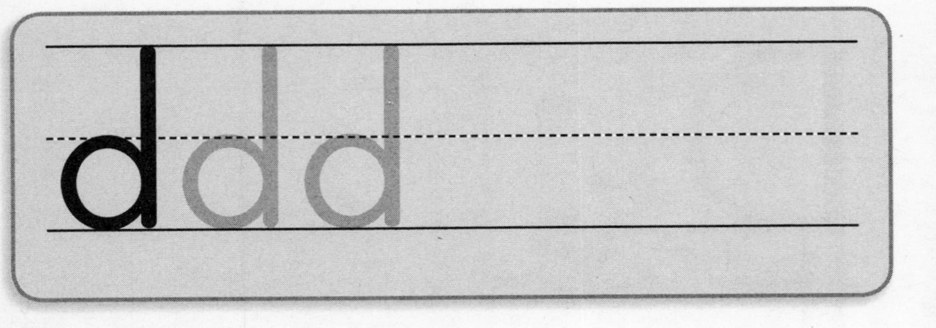

Go, Sam.

Go, Sam.

Name ____________________

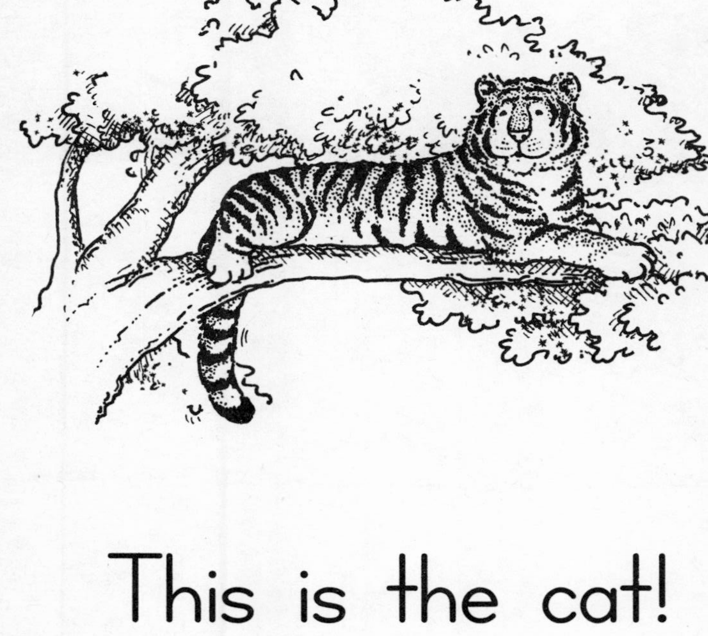

This is the cat!

This is the cat!

To the Teacher:

Have children reread the book, then write or trace the letters and words in the gray boxes.

This Cat

This is the  tail.

I I I

This is the  paw.

i i i

This is the  head.

is

Name ______________________________

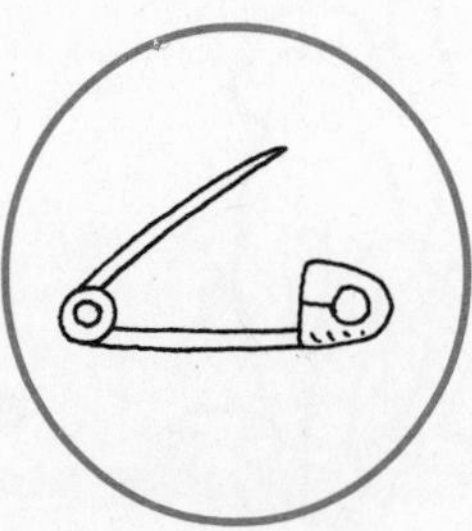

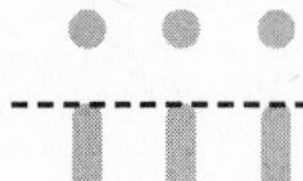

I I I

i i i

Phonics

 Say the picture names. If the picture name has the /i/ sound in the middle, circle the picture.

 Trace and write the letter *Ii*.

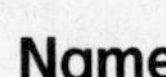

Name ____________________

1. This is a  .

2. This is a  .

3. This is a  .

4. This ____________ is a  .

High-Frequency Words

1: Read the sentence.

2–3: Read and trace the sentences.

4: Complete and read the sentence.

Name ______________________________

We [sleep] like this.

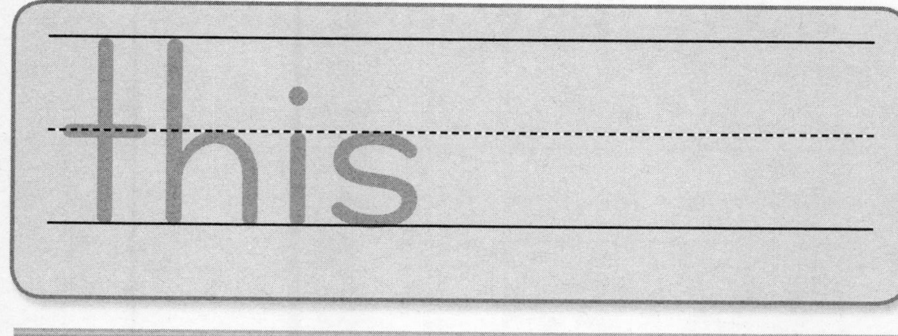

To the Teacher:
Have children reread the book, then write or trace the letters and words in the gray boxes.

Like This

We sit like this.

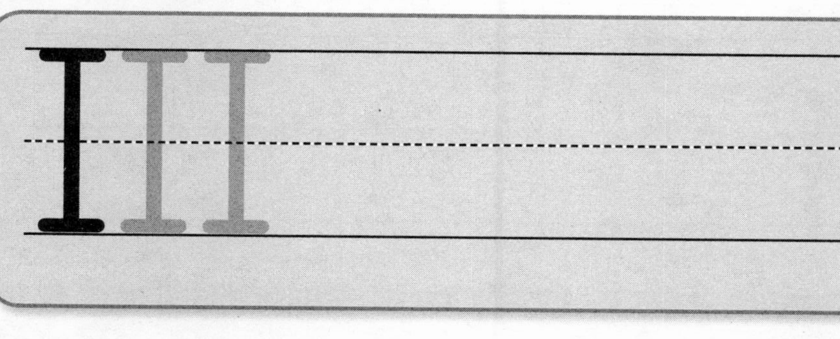

We climb like this.

We play like this.

Name ______________________

Rat and I [sleep].

To the Teacher:

Have children reread the book, then write or trace the letters and words in the gray boxes.

Rat and I

Rat and I sit.

Rat and I play.

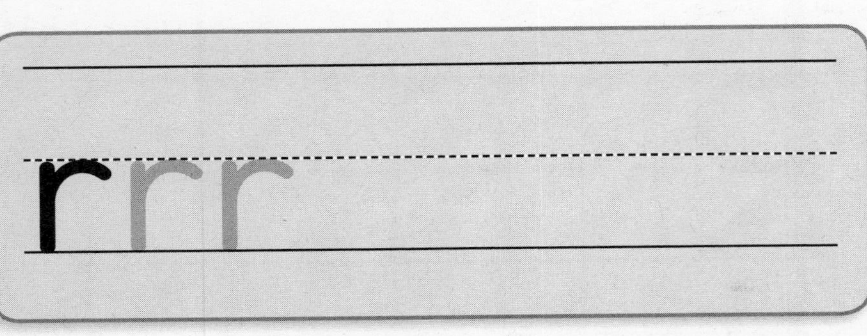

Rat and I 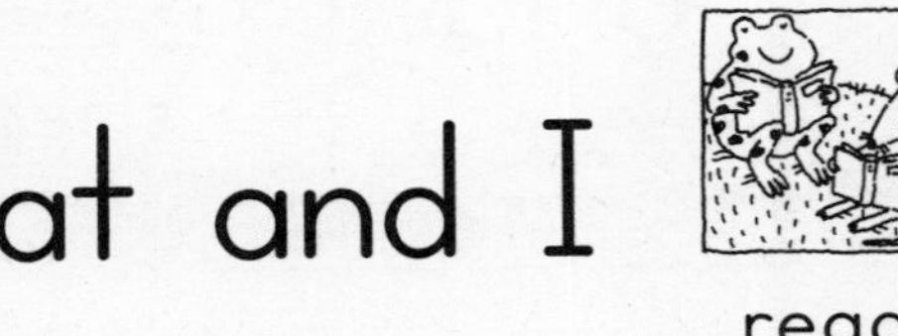  .
read

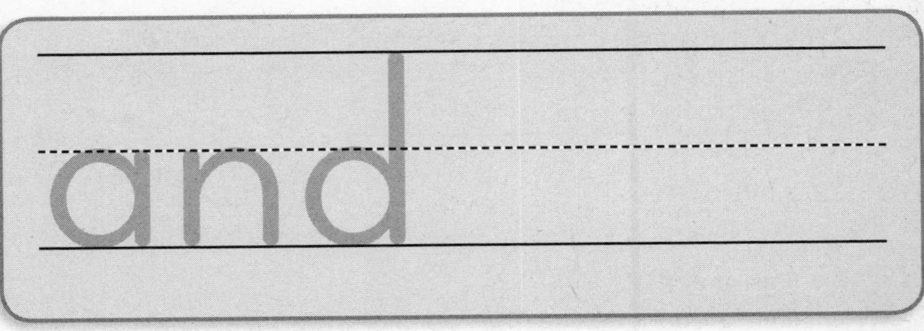

Name ____________________

 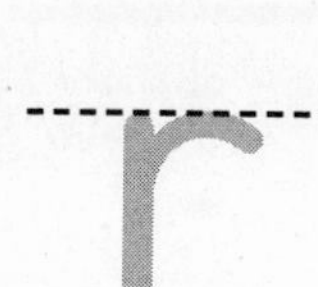
r

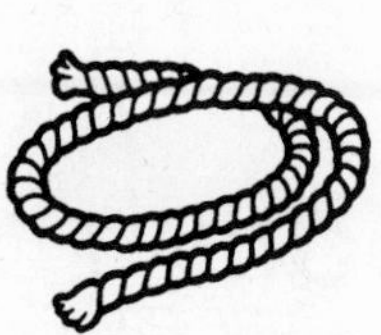 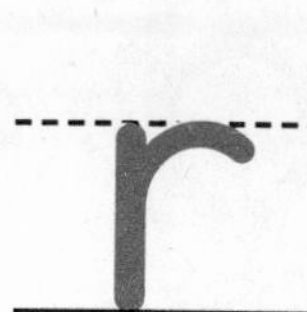
r

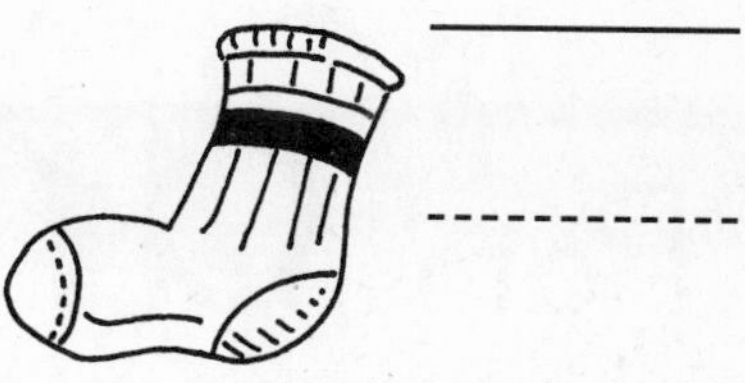

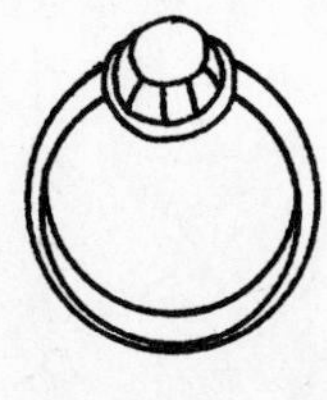 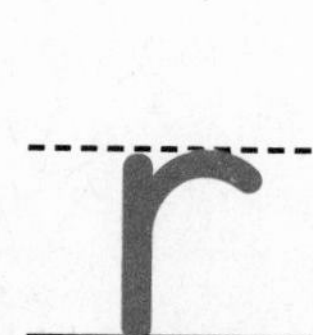
r

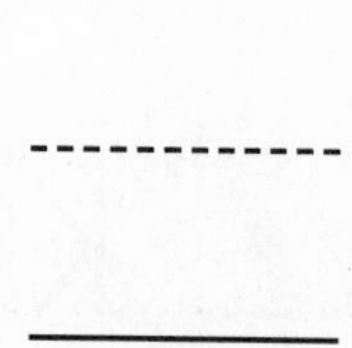 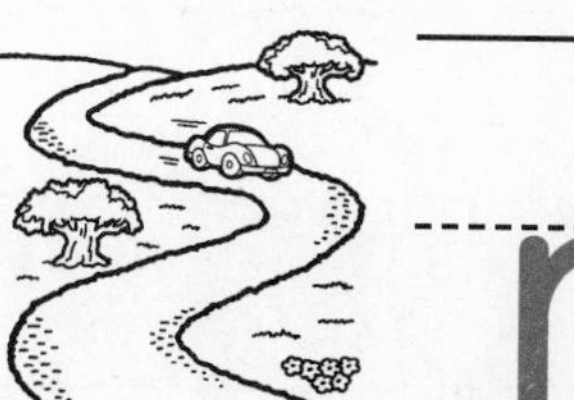
r

R R R

r r r

Phonics

 Say the picture names. If the picture name begins with the /r/ sound, write *r* on the line.

 Trace and write the letter *Rr*.

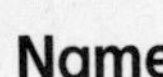

Name ______________________________

1. Pam and Sam ran.

2. Tip and Kit nap.

3. We sit and play.

4. Tim and Pat go!

High-Frequency Words

1: Read the sentence.

2: Trace the word *and* and read the sentence.

3–4: Complete and read the sentences.

Name ____________________

We ran and hid!

We ran and hid!

To the Teacher:
Have children reread the book, then write or trace the letters and words in the gray boxes.

We Hid

I ran and hid.

RRR

Dog ran and hid.

r r r

Rabbit ran and hid.

and

Name ______________________________

 are at bat.

Zebras

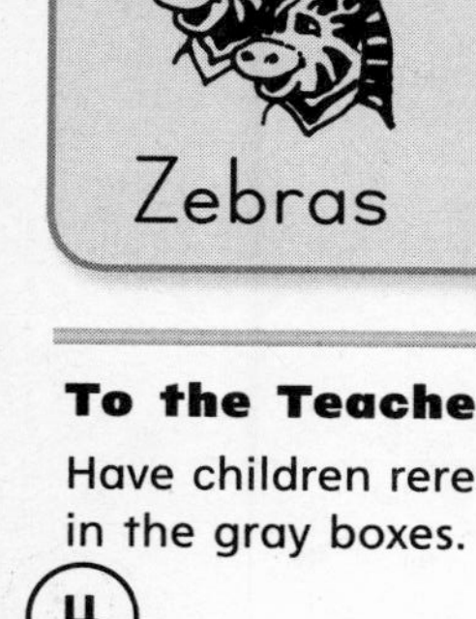 are at bat.

Zebras

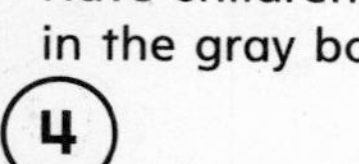

To the Teacher:

Have children reread the book, then write or trace the letters and words in the gray boxes.

At Bat

We are at bat.

B B B

Monkeys are at bat.

b b b

Tigers are at bat.

Name ______________________________

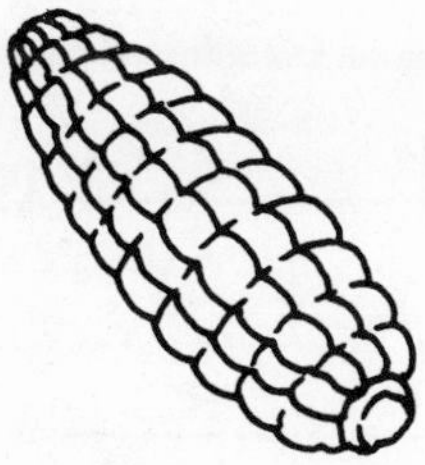

	c	o	b
	b	a	t
	b	i	b

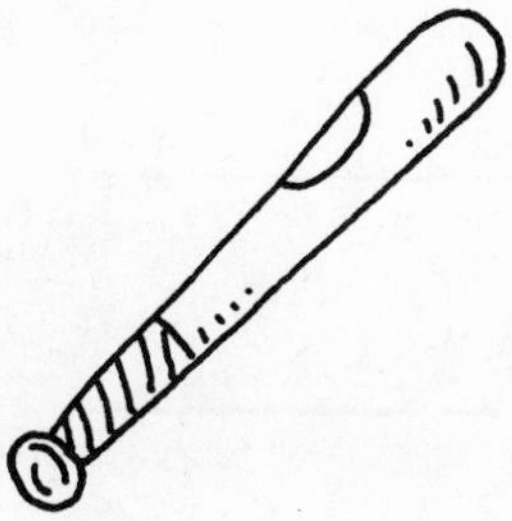

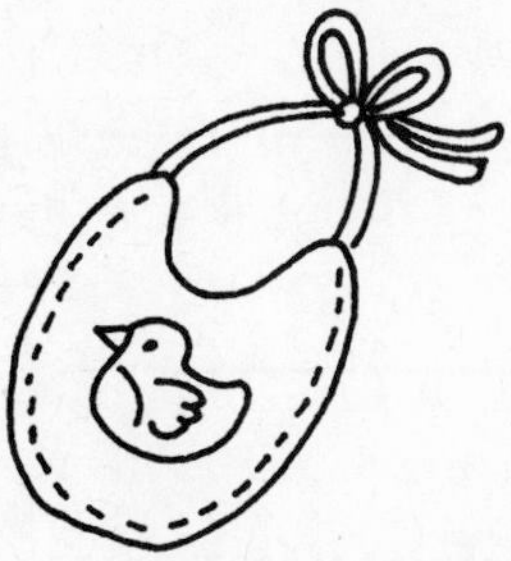

bat bad Bob

Phonics

 Say the picture name. Trace the letters on the lines. Write the missing vowel.

 Dictation: Write the following words: *bat, bad, Bob.*

Name ____________________

are

to

is

this

and

High-Frequency Words

Say and trace the word *are*. Then write the word. Then build the word with your Letter Cards. Repeat with the words *to*, *is*, *this*, and *and*.

Name ____________________

We are happy.

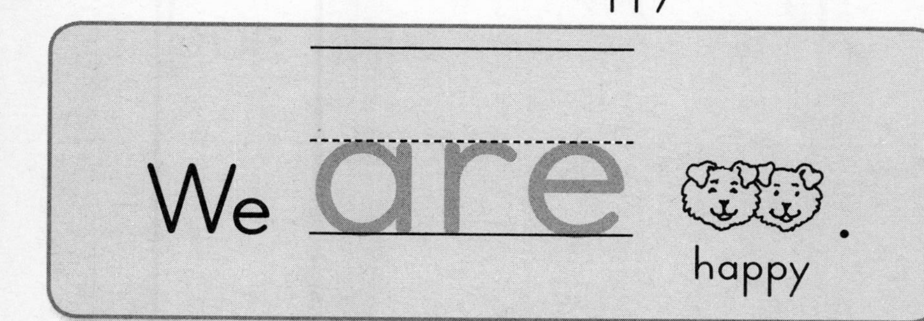

We are happy.

To the Teacher:
Have children reread the book, then write or trace the letters and words in the gray boxes.

Bad!

The dogs are bad.

B B B

The dogs are mad.

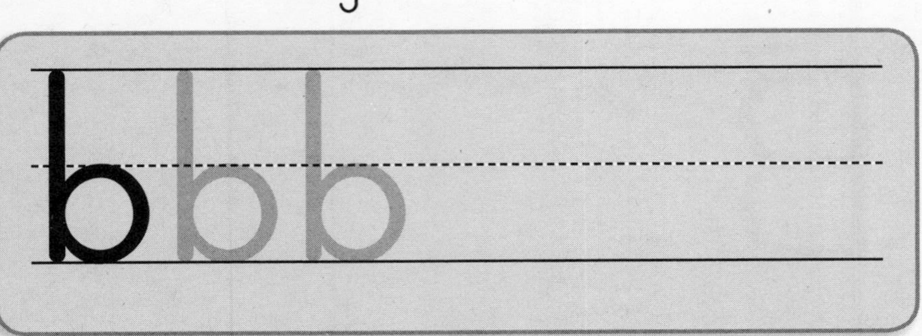

b b b

The  dogs are sad.

The dogs are sad.

Name ______________________

You are hot!

You are hot!

To the Teacher:
Have children reread the book, then write or trace the letters and words in the gray boxes.

Hot!

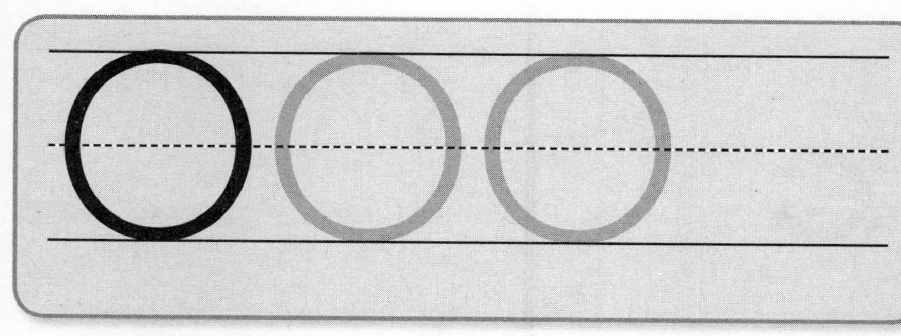

You can not hop.

o o o

You can not mop.

o o o

You can not bat.

Name ______________________________

p	o	t
t	o	p
m	o	p

hot not pop

Phonics

 Say the picture names. Write the word on the lines.

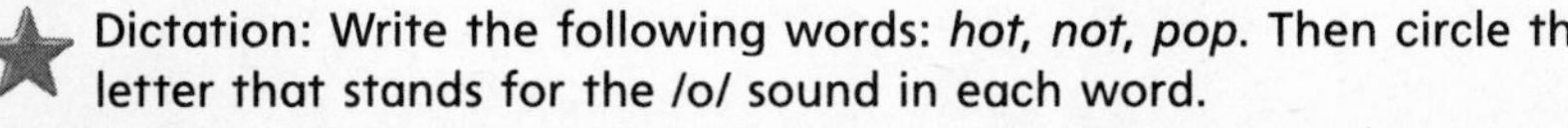

Dictation: Write the following words: *hot, not, pop*. Then circle the letter that stands for the /o/ sound in each word.

Name ______

you

are

and

this

is

High-Frequency Words

Say and trace the word *you*. Write the word. Then build the word with your Letter Cards. Repeat with the words *are*, *and*, *this*, and *is*.

Name ______________________

You are Tom!

You are Tom!

To the Teacher:

Have children reread the book, then write or trace the letters and words in the gray boxes.

Tom

Are you Tom?

O O O

You have the top.

O O O

You have the hat.

You have the hat.

Name ____________________

What a fat cat!

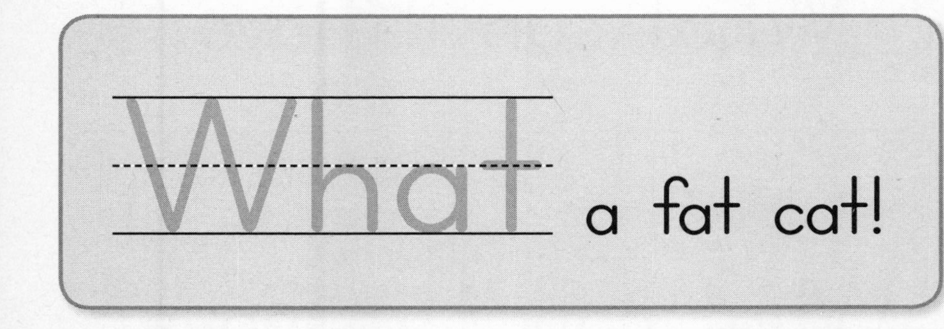

To the Teacher:
Have children reread the book, then write or trace the letters and words in the gray boxes.

Cat

A cat can lick.

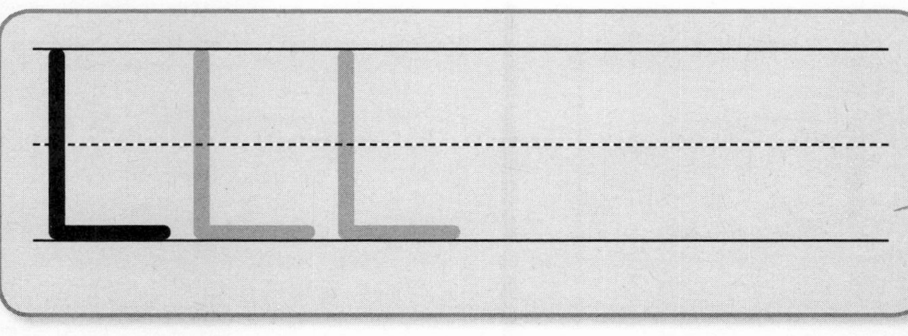

What can it play?

What can it have?

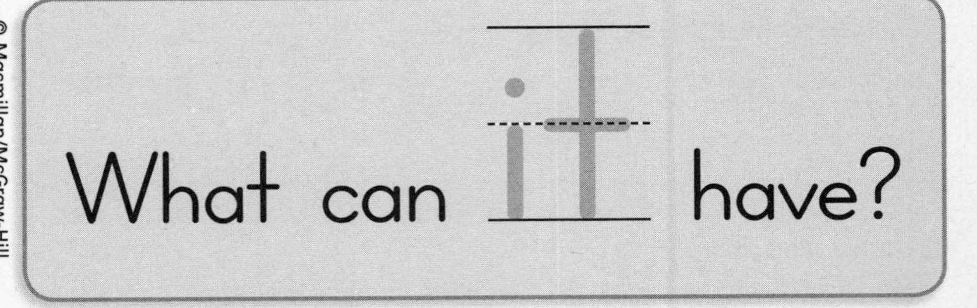

Name ______________________________

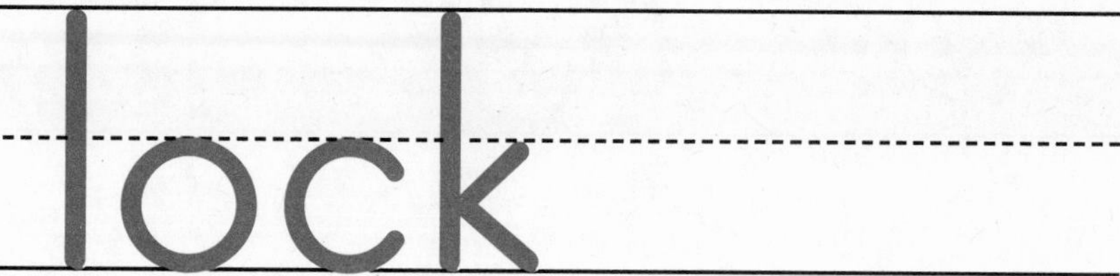

kick

tack

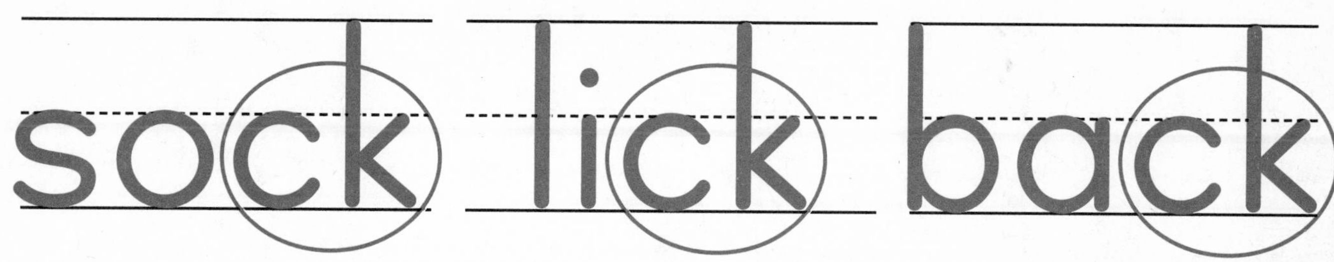

Phonics

 Say the picture name. Write the word on the line.

 Dictation: Write the following words: *sock, lick, back*. Then circle the letters that are the same in all three words.

Name ______________________________

What can I see?

What can I

see?

High-Frequency Words

Read the sentence. Look around you and draw something that you can see.
Then trace the sentence: *What can I see?*

Name ______________________

You can go!

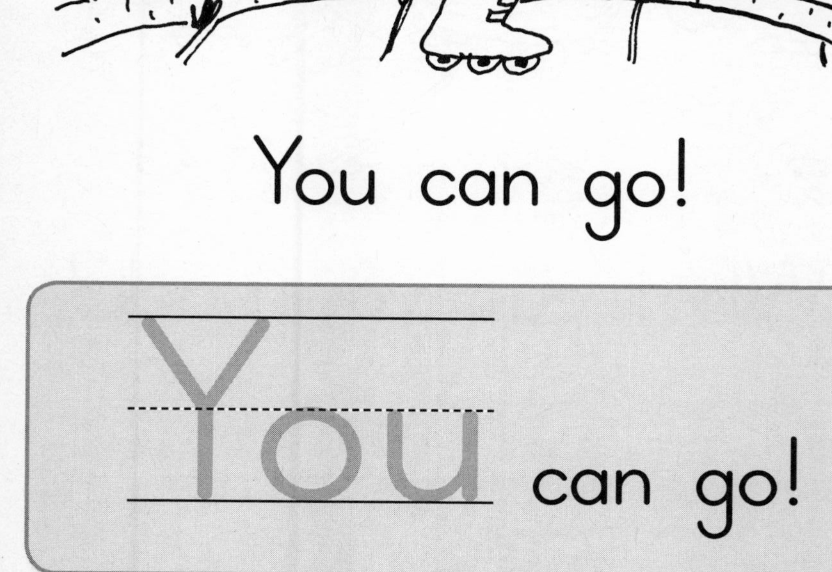

To the Teacher:
Have children reread the book, then write or trace the letters and words in the gray boxes.

A Kid Can

What can you kick?

What can you hit?

k k k

What can you pack?

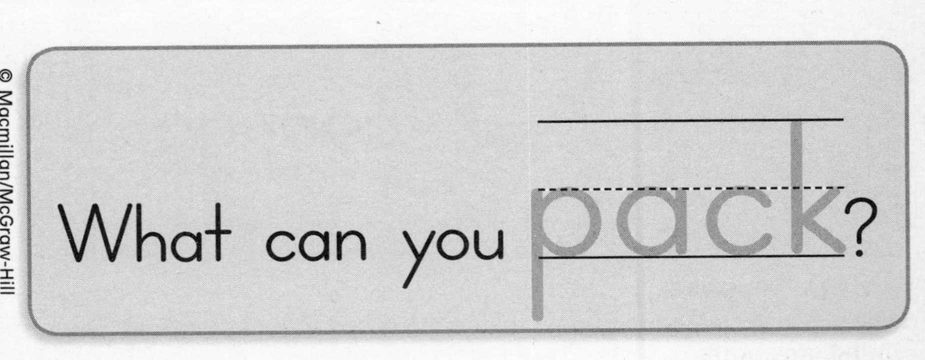

Name ____________________

Lad and Dot play.

Lad and Dot play.

To the Teacher:
Have children reread the book, then write or trace the letters and words in the gray boxes.

Lad and Dot

Are you Lad?

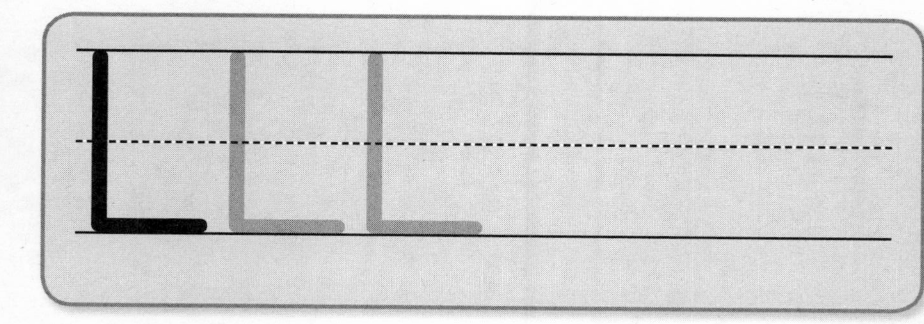

Are you Dot?

Lad and Dot hop.

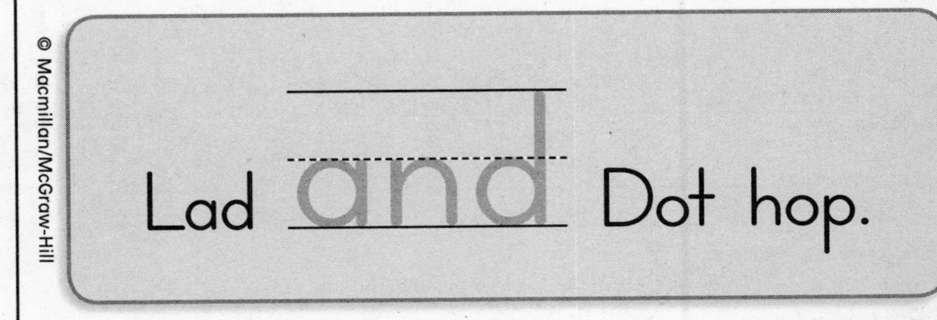

Name ____________________

Tom has a 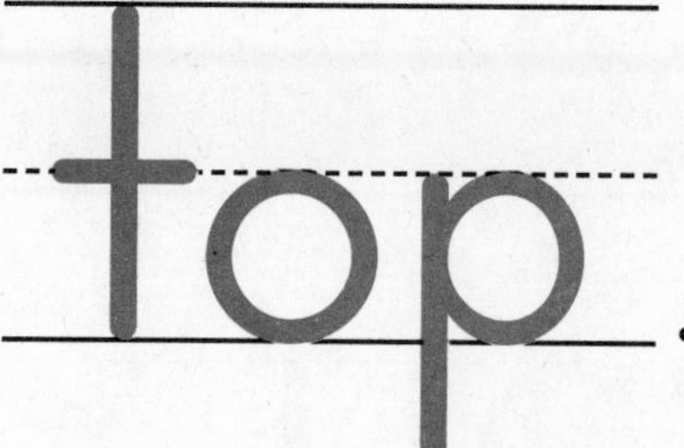 .

mop

I see the sock.

sick

The pot is  .

dot

top sock 

Phonics

 Look at the picture. Read the sentence. Circle the word that tells about the picture. Write the word.

 Now write the words you chose. Circle the letter that is the same in all three words.

Write

Name ____________________

you	what	are	and

1. you
2. what
3. are
4. and

1. I see you.
2. I see Tom and the cat.

High-Frequency Words

 Read the words in the box. Write one word on each line.

 Use a word from the box to finish each sentence.

Name ____________________

This is a sock!

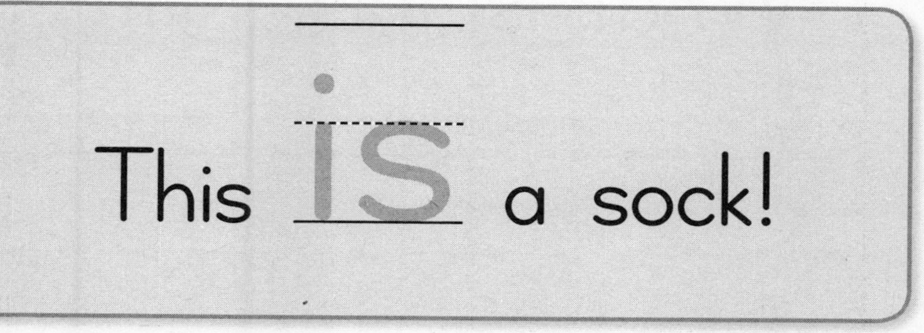

This is a sock!

To the Teacher:
Have children reread the book, then write or trace the letters and words in the gray boxes.

Kit and Kim

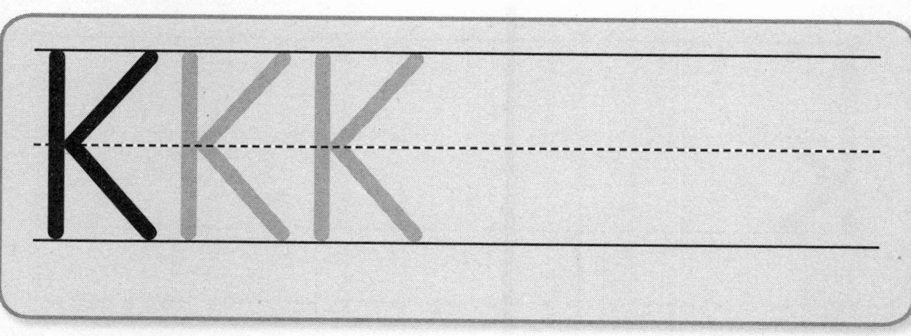

What is this, Kit?

K K K

This is a rock!

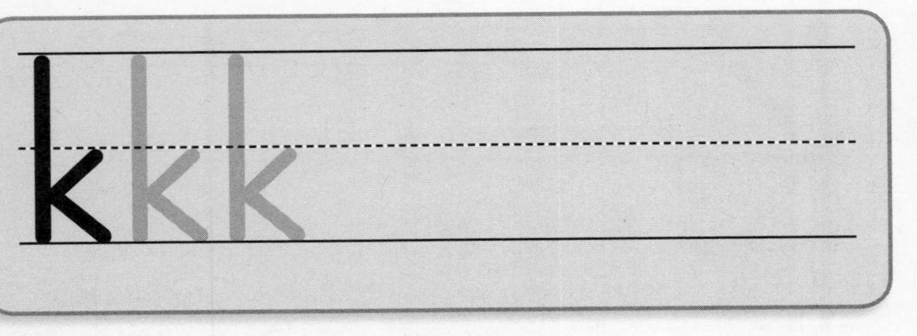

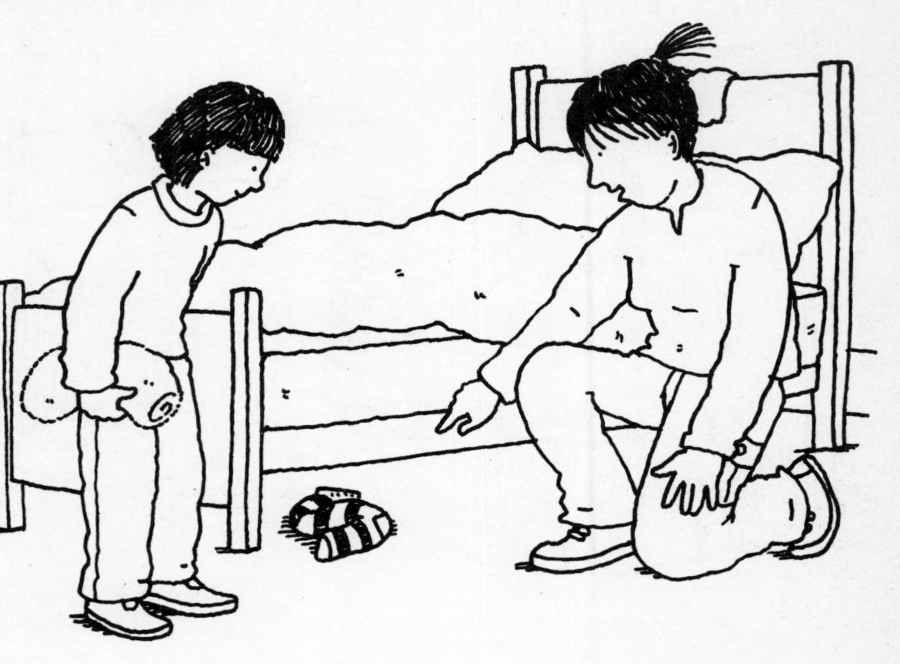

What is this, Kim?

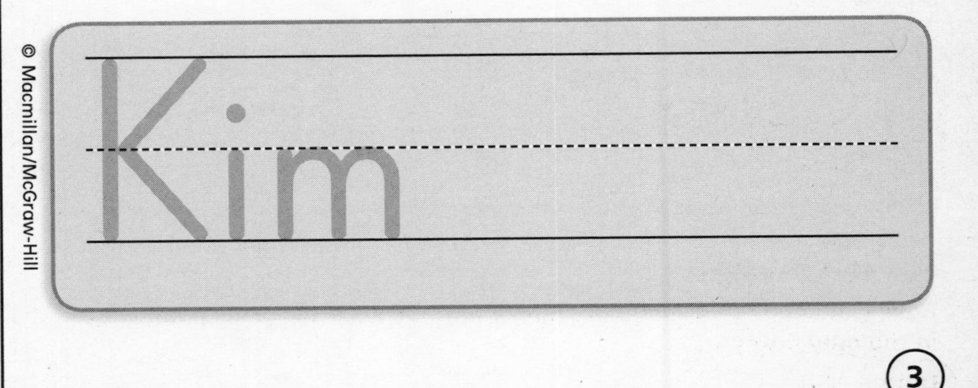

Name ______________________

Can a hen do it?

Can a hen do it?

To the Teacher:
Have children reread the book, then write or trace the letters and words in the gray boxes.

A Hen and a Cat

A hen can do this.

E E E

Can a cat do it?

A cat can do this.

Name ________________________________

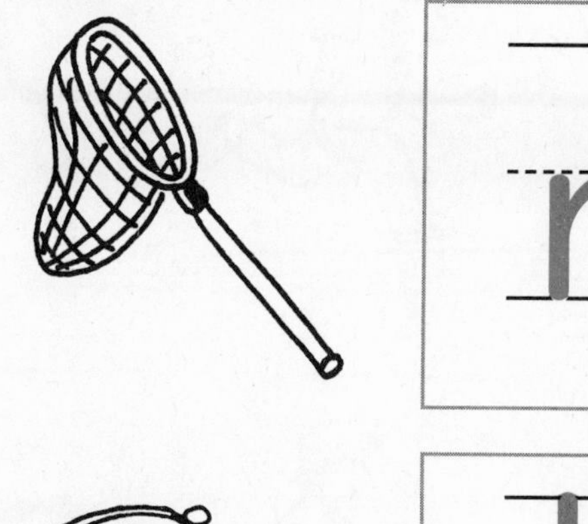

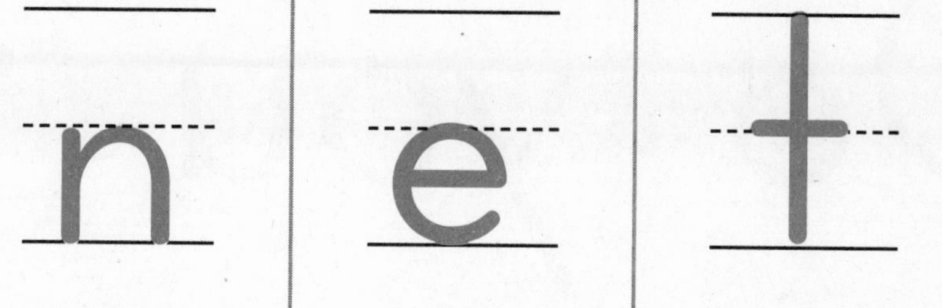

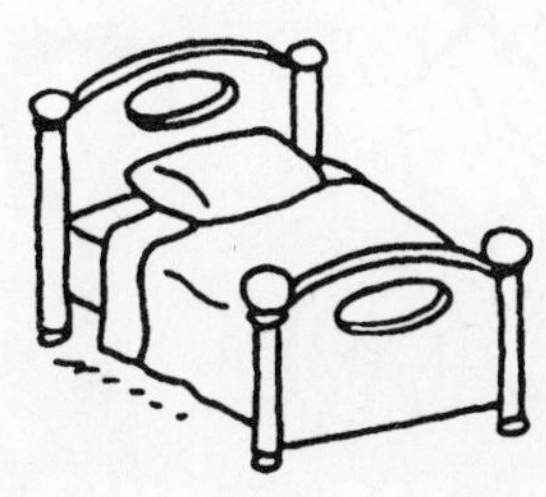

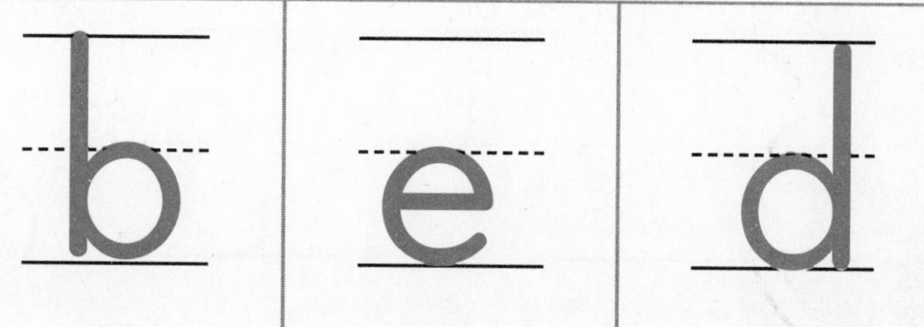

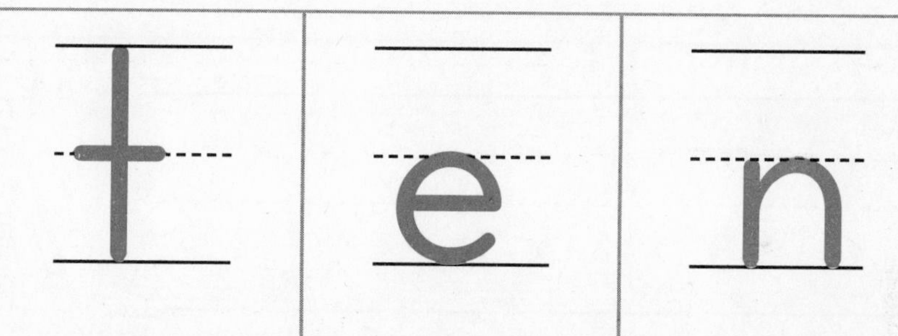

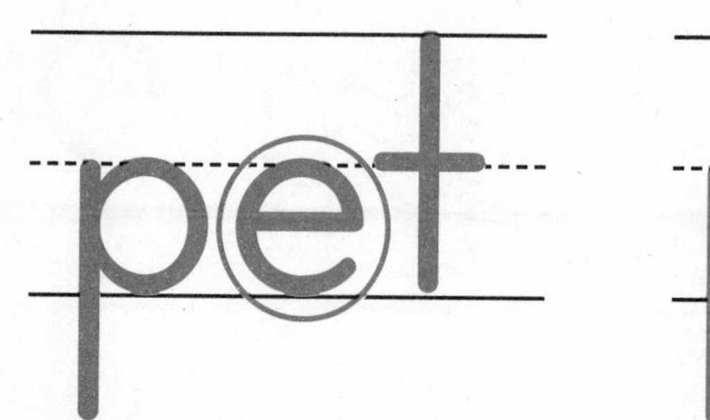

Phonics

 Say the picture names. Write the words on the lines.

 Dictation: Write the following words: *pet, pen, red.* Then circle the letters that are the same in the words.

Name ___

1. Do you  ?

2.   ?

3.   ?

4. 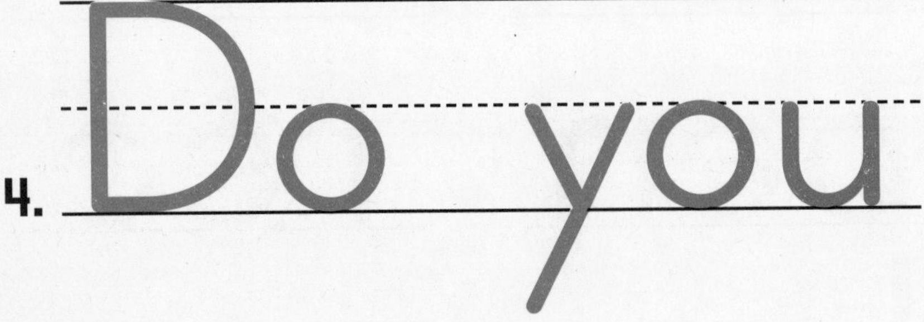  ?

High-Frequency Words

1: Read the question.

2–3: Read and trace the questions.

4: Write the question and then read it.

Name ____________________

What is in the pen?

What is in the pen?

To the Teacher:
Have children reread the book, then write or trace the letters and words in the gray boxes.

A Den and a Pen

Do you see a den?

E E E

What is in the den?

Do you see a pen?

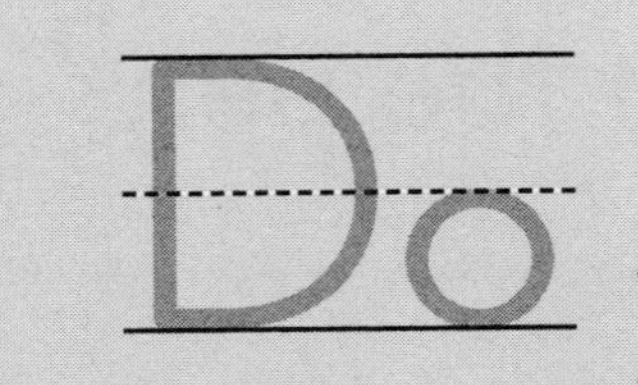

you see a pen?

Name ____________________

"We can go!" said Pam.

"We can go!"

To the Teacher:
Have children reread the book, then write or trace the letters and words in the gray boxes.

Ed and Pam

"Get on," said Ed.

"I am on," said Pam.

g g g

"Can we go?" said Ed.

Name ______________________________

w i g

d o g

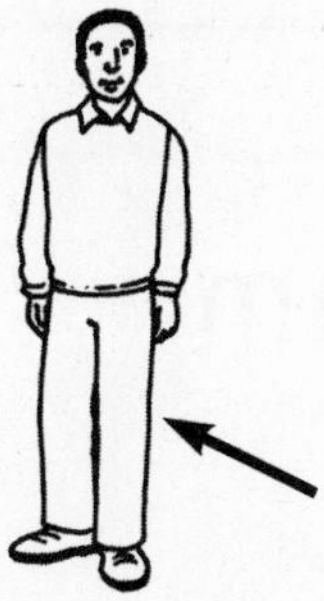

l e g

big dig wet

Phonics

 Say the picture names. Write the words on the lines.

 Dictation: Write the following words: *big, dig, wet.*

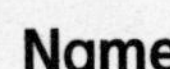

Name ______________________________

1. "Sit," said Tim.

2. "Go, go, go!" said Dad.

3. "I see you," said Sam.

4. "You can play," said Meg.

High-Frequency Words

1: Read the sentence.

2: Read the sentence and trace the word *said*.

3–4: Write the word *said* to finish the sentences.

Name ____________

"I got wet!" said Mom.

said

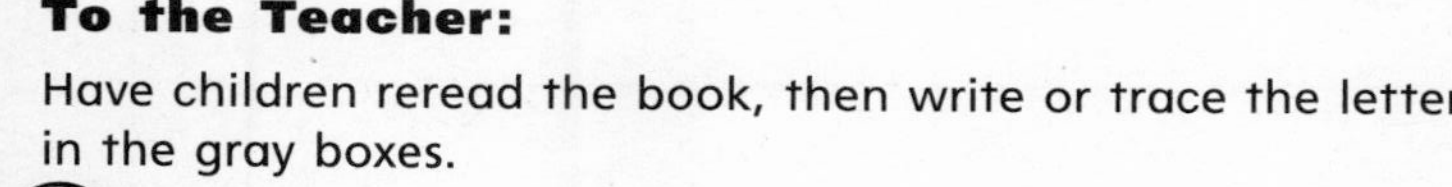

To the Teacher:
Have children reread the book, then write or trace the letters and words in the gray boxes.

Did Kim Win?

"Did I win?" said Kim.

W W W W

"You did win!" said Mom.

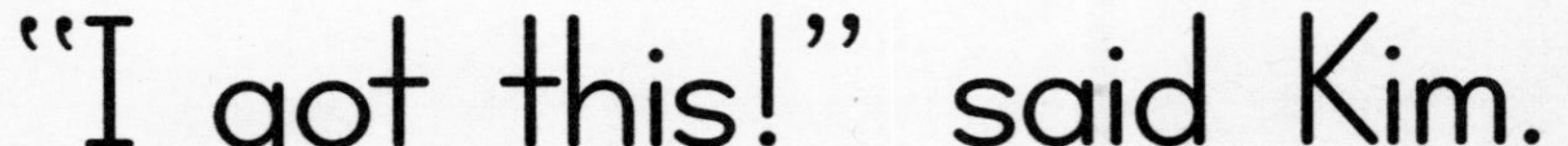

"I got this!" said Kim.

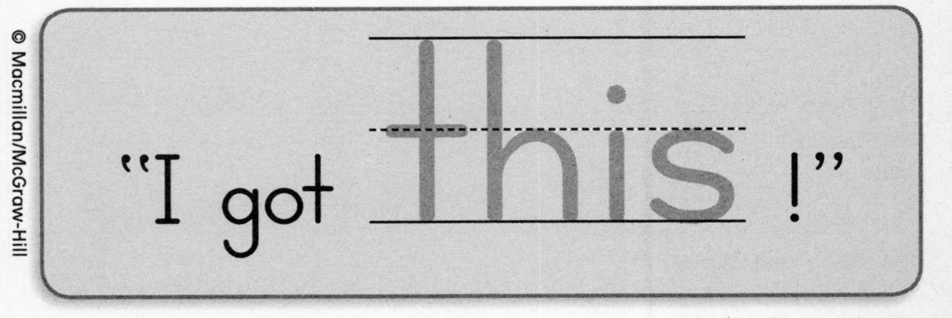

Name ______________________

"I am six!"

To the Teacher:

Have children reread the book, then write or trace the letters and words in the gray boxes.

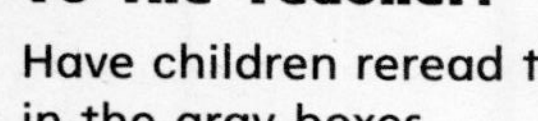

Max

"Max is here," said Mom.

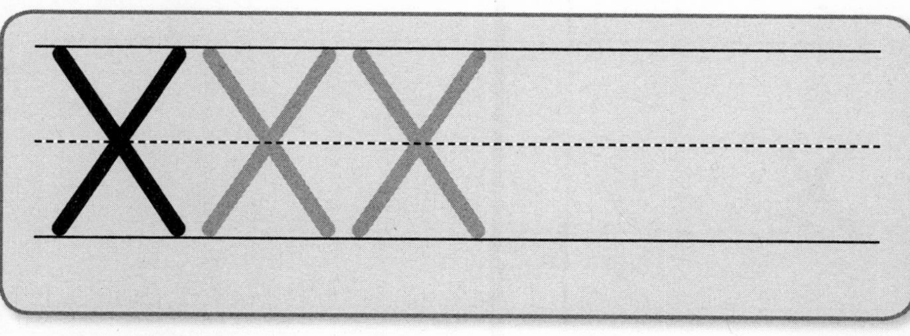

"Can you fix it?"

"I can fix it," said Max.

Name ____________________

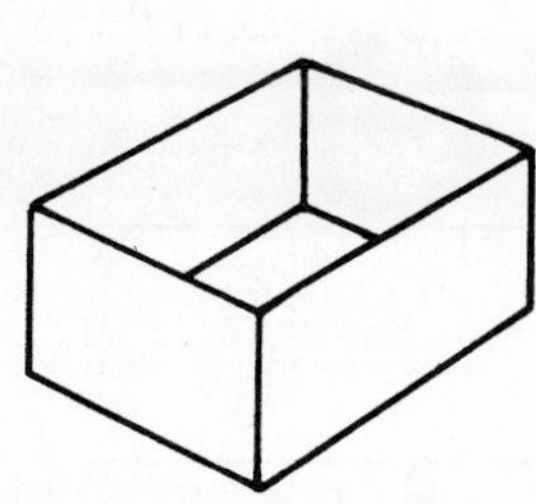 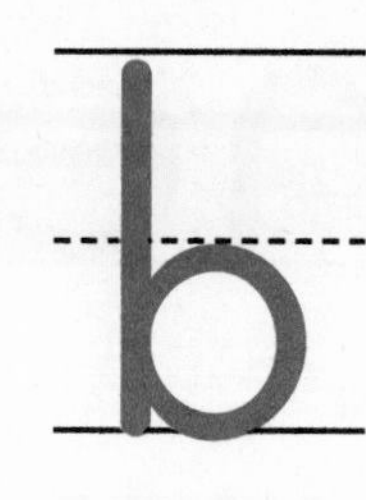 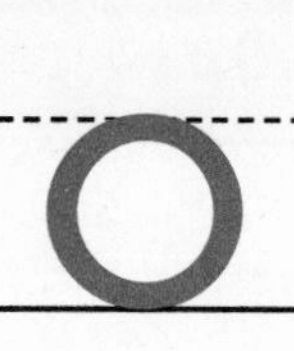 

 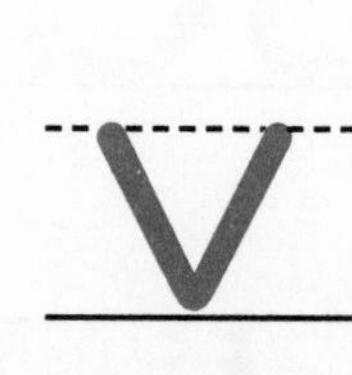  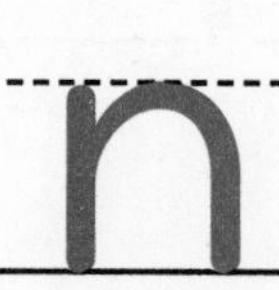

 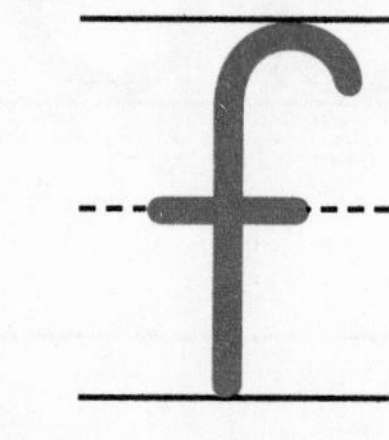  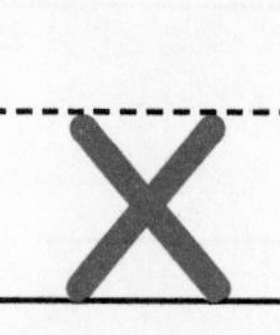

I sat in a van.

Phonics

 Say the picture names. Write the words on the lines.

 Dictation: Write the following sentence: *I sat in a van.*

Name ______________________________

here here

said said

do do

you you

and and

High-Frequency Words

Say and trace the word *here*. Then write the word. Then build the word with your Letter Cards. Repeat with the words: *said*, *do*, *you*, and *and*.

Name ____________________

Sit here, Val!

Sit here, Val!

To the Teacher:

Have children reread the book, then write or trace the letters and words in the gray boxes.

Val

Val is a vet.

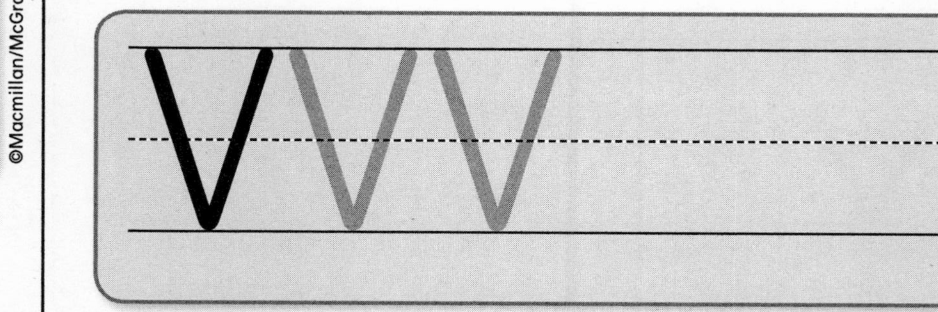

V V V

"Sit here," said Val.

"Sit here," said Val.

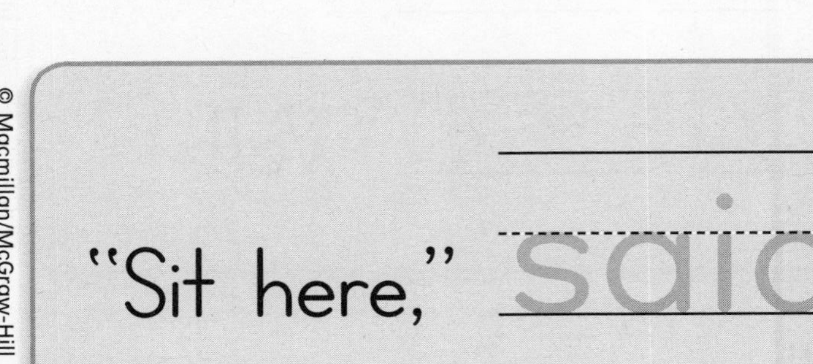

Name ______________________

Look in the tub.

Can you see 4?

To the Teacher:

Have children reread the book to a family member.

Duck, Duck, Duck

Look in the mud.

Can you see 1 duck?

Look in the hut.

Can you see 2?

Look at the rug.

Can you see 3?

Name ______________________________

cup	bus	run	bug

1. cup

2. bus

3. run

4. bug

Phonics

Write each word from the box in order on each line. Draw a line from the word to the matching picture.

Name ______________________________

1. We look at the sun.

2. Pam can look in.

3. Do I look sad?

4. We look at a play.

High-Frequency Words

1: Read the sentence.

2: Read the sentence and trace the word *look*.

3–4: Write the word *look* and read the sentences.

Name ________________

Look at the 4 men.

The men run and

have fun.

©Macmillan/McGraw-Hill

To the Teacher:

Have children reread the book to a family member.

A Fun Run

Look at the ten men.

The men have fun.

Look at the 2 men.

The men run in

the mud.

Look at the 3 men.

The men run in

the sun.

Name ____________________

Jim is not little.
Jim and Jen are
big, big, big!

To the Teacher:
Have children reread the book to a family member.

Jim and Jen

Jim is little.
Jen is big.

"Have a little,"
said Jim.
"Have a lot,"
said Jen.

"I like this!"
said Jim.
"I like this!"
said Jen.

Name ______________________________

jug quack zip

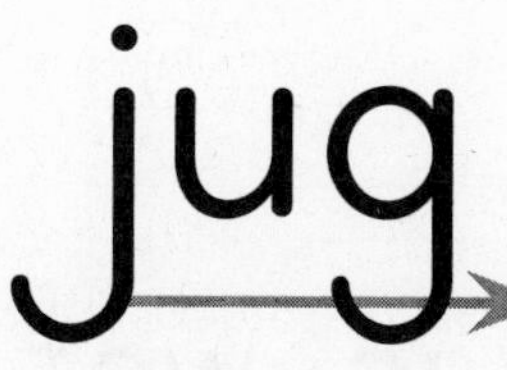

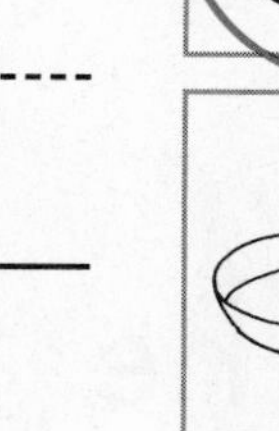

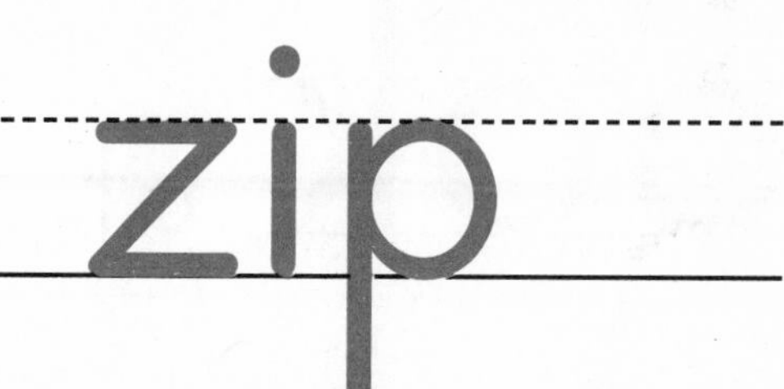

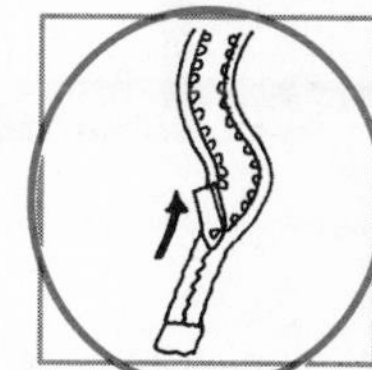

Phonics

Blend the sounds and say the word. Write the word. Circle the picture that shows the word. Say the word again.

Write

Name ______________________________

do	look	here	little

1. do
2. look
3. here
4. little

1. The little dog is wet.
2. Look at the big pig.

High-Frequency Words

 Read the words in the box. Write one word on each line.

 Use a word from the box to finish each sentence.

Name ____________________

Quack and Zip play.

Quack and Zip run

and quack.

To the Teacher:

Have children reread the book to a family member.

Quack and Zip

This is Quack.

Quack is a little duck.

This is Zip.

Zip is a little dog.

"Are you quick?"

said Quack.

"Can you quack?"

said Zip.

Name ______________________

What do you see here?

To the Teacher:
Have children reread the book to a family member.

Look!

Look at this .

You can see it here.

Look at this ▲.

Can you see it here?

Look at this ●.

Do you see it yet?

Name ________________________________

 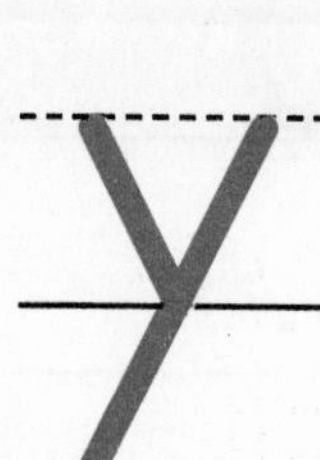

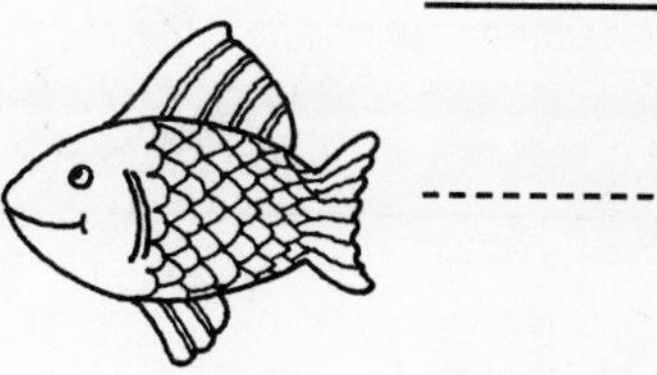

 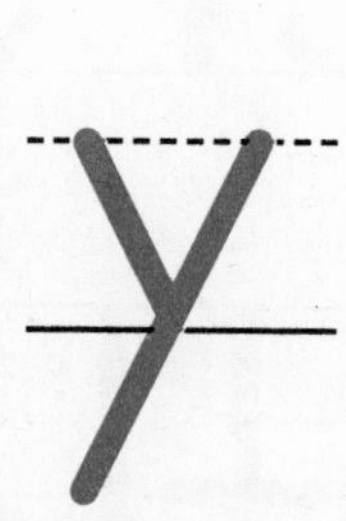
 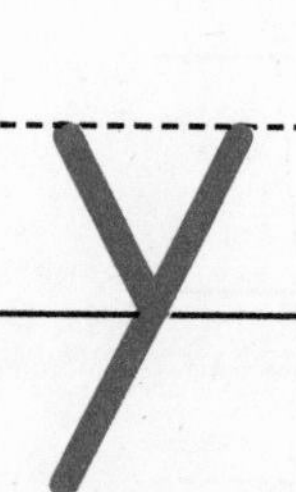
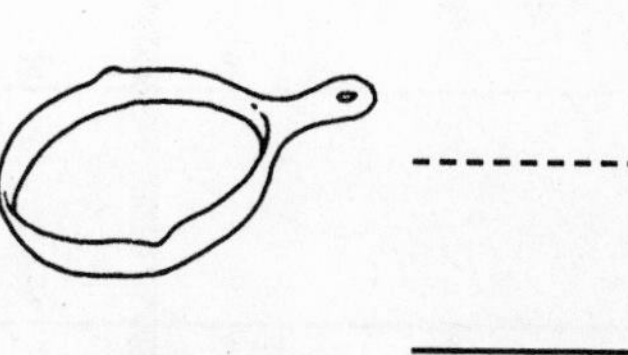

Phonics

 Say the picture names. If the picture name begins with the /y/ sound, write *y* on the line.

 Trace and write the letter *Yy*.

Name ______________________________

do do

here here

little little

look look

said said

High-Frequency Words

Say and trace the word *do*. Write the word. Then build the word with your Letter Cards. Repeat with the words *here*, *little*, *look*, and *said*.

Name ______________________________

Do you see this ?

What can you  draw ?

To the Teacher:
Have children reread the book to a family member.

You Can!

Do you see this ?

What can you  draw ?

Look!

You can sit on it!

Look!

You can go in it!